the noble savage

published by MERIDIAN BOOKS, INC. New York

2

Subscription orders should be addressed to THE NOBLE SAVAGE
Meridian Books, Inc., 12 East 22 Street, New York 10, N.Y.
One-year subscription (2 issues): $2.75. Single copy: $1.50.
THE NOBLE SAVAGE *is published twice yearly, in Spring and Fall.*
Manuscripts will not be returned unless accompanied by
stamped, self-addressed envelope.

Distributed in Great Britain and the Commonwealth except
Canada by Weidenfeld & Nicolson, 20 New Bond Street,
London, W.1. 12/6 per copy.

M

A MERIDIAN PERIODICAL
Published by Meridian Books, Inc. October 1960
First printing September 1960

Library of Congress Catalog Card Number: 60-9654
Typography and design by Elaine Lustig
Manufactured in the United States of America

VON BRAUN IN PURGATORY

Wernher von Braun, Director, Development Operations Division, Army Ballistic Missile Agency, has written an article for *This Week* which the Sunday supplement called "one of the most inspiring articles on the subject you will ever read." The subject was "Why Should America Conquer Space?" and the conclusion is that knowledge is uplifting to the spirit, potentially profitable, and provides one of the frontiers at which we meet the Chinese and the Russians. Among the insights with which Mr. von Braun inspired his readers was a local color joke about how "space is a pretty big place—they say it is even bigger than Texas and Alaska." And he quoted Winston Churchill on the space challenge: "All he could offer them was blood, sweat, and tears," remarking that this remark got remarked "during the last war, when I was on the other side."

It is tempting to exhibit more of the quality of his inspiring words, such as: "Dark clouds are rapidly moving up. I fear it is later than we think. I am profoundly worried as to what has happened to the American frontier spirit."

Along the way of making his argument, Mr. von Braun also recalled the days when he was head of the Nazi rocket program, still regaling his readers with an account of "what I thought was a ringing appeal for a determined U.S. space program," which "got a big hand."

> During the ensuing question-and-answer period someone got up and demanded: "Why are you telling us all that? Weren't you connected with the development of the Nazi V-2 rockets that fell on London during the last war?"
>
> All I could answer was that having survived one dictatorship I didn't want my own American-born children nor anyone else's to live under another. Maybe I should have said it seems that you must have passed through purgatory to appreciate heaven.

The logic here seems to sputter on its launching pad. Just who was in purgatory when Mr. von Braun was devising his V-2 rockets? Wernher von Braun or the people of London? Mr. von Braun suavely identifies the slaughtered victim with the executioner; this makes for bad symbolic drama and provides, from the mouth of an expert, another insult to the dead, who are perhaps accustomed to insult.

The living might take notice, however, of who is speaking for "the American frontier spirit . . . where people laugh and enjoy God's world more than anywhere else."

THE SEEING EYE

Some time ago an ad appeared in *The New York Times*, large enough to make the visual shock impressive, of a bus and several burning cars at the scene of an appalling accident. The caption under this photograph read:

READ ABOUT IT BEFORE THEY TOW THE CARS AWAY!

The ad went on to say that in the vital fast-moving world in which we now live (and die) the reader couldn't afford to wait till tomorrow to learn about the events that happened today. The event pictured—one of the worst of its kind—derived both its importance and news value from the fact that it was captured before the cars had been towed away.

What appetite, perhaps we should say what lust, is being gratified in this manner? Do we have, today, a pornography of violence? Are these *hot* snapshots of meaningless horror the equivalent of the breasts and thighs, the human poultry display that ornaments our news racks? Does the look somehow gratify what the sensation itself seems to withhold? There is no end of sex in America, but the hunger for the look of sex appears to increase, rather than decrease, with the decline of the taboos. There is no end of violence in America, both before and after the cars are towed away, but the lust for violence remains ungratified by the event itself. We seem to feel, with the criminal, a compulsion to return to the scene of the crime.

Has the camera eye, with its command to LOOK, and the LOOK that increasingly commands our attention, made it possible for us to look without seeing anything? Do we have at our disposal, today, a nonseeing eye? Strange as it seems, the scene of the disaster and the anonymous nude perform the same function—seen through the nonseeing eye they supply the thrill without the risks. The reassurance we seem to need that we are alive, and that life can be seen going on around us, we get in the form of visual shock capsules. The viewer himself supplies the shock-absorbers. There is nothing like death—nothing like somebody else's—to remind the man who doubts that he is really *living*, that he is, in most respects, still very much alive.

The magazine writer, with the photographer in tow, goes from room to room in John Doe's new house, looks over the gadgets and peers under the beds, and coyly probes into the teen-ager's sex life. The magazine consultant, like the visiting nurse, probes the inhabitants for cavities that need treatment—but a cavity worth probing is a private thing. The pleasure-pain is reserved for a private tongue. Cavities, like diaries, are hard to breed in a doorless home. At what point does the private world of Picasso assume more importance than his painting—at what point, that is, does the public feel entitled to it? The question itself defines a new conception of privacy. It is the last commodity that a man has to sell. It parallels a now old-fashioned notion of virginity. Revelation illuminates privacy and explains why it is that life is empty without it—exposure merely reduces such privacy as we have. It leaves us, naturally, with a lust for what we have relinquished. Anyone who claims to have it we turn to, with appetite.

In this fashion, the pathology of the Peeping Tom becomes the license of a new profession—if the *Life* photographer knocks on the door, someone opens it. What is an inside story without somebody's insides? It is the camera that takes the picture, and it is the data that assures the voyeur he is not being cheated—for that is how he feels.

These men are under orders, *our* orders, to get the shot. Our appetite being what it is, we require these shots in ever stronger doses—our visual diet is nonvegetarian, we like our meat rare. To supply this carnivore with his supply of raw meat the news hound acts as a species of vulture, swooping down to *cover* the scene of the accident. We want the bloom of it, and what we want we get. When we ask ourselves by what potion we have come to such a pass, it is by appetite, first, and second, by degrees. If each day you increase the dosage, each day you reduce the effect. Not too long ago the words *horrible accident* would have been more than enough. A picture, any picture, would have been considered barbarous. Now we lust to be there before the bodies are carted away. With the accumulation of these pointless exposures the mind becomes a portable waste basket—a news file where the shockers are stored for future reference. Such a clogged mind naturally cries out for a periodic housecleaning, a burning of useless debris to make room for more of it. This burning we get, in a vicarious form, from the eyewitness reports of senseless conflagrations, the wide-scale ruin of hurricanes and floods, or those atomic explosions that actually change the face of the earth. Such awesome sights seem to purge the exhausted mind of its waste material, and restore, for a brief moment, the power of sensation.

The disappearance of a private life of our own generates in us a lust for the private lives of others. By sympathetic magic we hope to absorb it through our eyes. Picture magazines, movies, documentary studies, and the mindless eye of the newsreel camera, all feed this craving for the private life of somebody *else*. Anybody. It matters less now than it once did that this carrion we feed on is famous or unknown. We hardly care so long as we are fed on the private parts. Our appetite for these details is insatiable. Eating habits, sleeping habits, active and inactive leisure habits, reading, talking, fighting, and loving habits, all are tossed into the maw of our lust for life. For that, in substance, is what it is.

We say the camera never lies, but it were truer to say that it cannot tell the truth. The truth is a concept, and the camera cannot conceive. If and when it does it will no longer be a camera. It will be a human, like the rest of us, suffer from delusions, migraine, and fallout, expiring before its time from the abuses of a world it is obliged to face. But for the time being *that* model is not available. The camera buyer must still supply the seeing-eye himself.

It is this eye, faced with the meaningless event, that transforms it into meaning. Out of the scene's incoherence a sense of coherence can be seen to emerge. It may well bring a message to chill the heart, or feed a lust that is better unmentioned, but it will not stand idle while the cars are being towed away.

PEACE AND HARMONY

Those who have been happily wrapping their arms around the millennium all because of the proliferation of FM stations devoted (among other things) to the playing of high-class music might try listening a little harder. Reservations might arise. It isn't just that many of the programs sound as though they might have been produced in the offices of *The New Yorker* or *Holiday*—the clear-eyed young American couple vacationing hand in hand through Devon with Purcell piping softly in the middle distance and the little Triumph waiting discreetly in the background. That's the least of it.

Pay attention to the canned voice of Mayor Wagner calling American mothers to arms over WNYC every evening at chamber-music time. *This is Maya Wagna. I am concoined about juvenile deliquency and I believe that with your help we can stamp it out. If you do not know where your children are, it may be time to re-evaluate your responsibilities.*

In her graciously appointed East Harlem apartment, the Puerto Rican mother, stretched out on the broadloom in her toreador pants, flicks the ash from her Du Maurier and re-evaluates her responsibilities to her children, sharpening their switchblades in the alley while she composes herself before the stereo for Kempff and the Beethoven Op. 111.

The FM stations have been superimposed on an existing mess, like a battle-ribbon Band-Aid on an infected finger; the cultural topography resembles an army engineers' map revealing, one atop the other, variations in terrain, housing, communications, weather. We begin to discern the outlines of an order in which hi-fi, social satire, and *Dissent* can co-habit with mass poverty, wretchedness, and degeneration not only in the same nation but in the same state. There is no law against cultural miscegenation, nor even any embarrassment, to prevent FM and gracious living from co-existing in West Virginia with ragged, shivering children. Nor has there been anguish or outcry from either camp so far, from those profiting from the cultural upsurge in the booming housing developments of West Virginia, or from their very near neighbors, the miners and their families who, as their Governor insists, are not actually starving but merely hungry. One seems not only willing, but ready and able to tolerate and support the continued existence of the other. The two worlds exist, not just side by side, but one atop the other, and as the frequencies are modulated, the sounds of quiet misery are overcome by the soothing static-free strains of madrigals and canzoni d'amore.

ISLANDS IN THE SUN

By now I imagine most of us have seen those chic ads of the Islands in the Sun Club and have taken comfort from the fact that for the likes of Cleveland Amory there are still refuges from the harsh realities of American life where the trade winds blow, the natives remain picturesque, the ceremonies colorful, the real estate uncluttered, and anthropology uncomplicated. But how many of us are aware of the fantastic ironies involved in these islands of misery and brilliance, or revolution, anticolonialism, and anti-Americanism, becoming America's playgrounds of the future? What kind of place to play or buy a beach! Unless you like to live where history leaves a bad taste in the mouth, and not merely a faint mark in the memory.

But perhaps we should all join. They are good microcosms of some of the problems our children will have to face, if not ourselves. For irony's sake, consider the images we could see from our beachcombers *bohio:* the waddling-fleshed hausfrau past her best, her thighs rivulets of veins and her breasts yeasty growths of mold; her companion lapdog, her husband, hung with hardware, toting the loot, his wallet oozing from his hip like the cigar from his lip; and next to them, not the picturesque native, vigorous and black, banging his drums, but the young engineer, dressed with a snobbery these same tourists will affect when they return to New York or London, a regimental tie in the furnace of noon and locked up in his breast such thoughts that did the tourists but guess them they would turn belly-up in the tide that brought them; and next to him, a beautiful woman, erect in carriage, bound in a flaming bandanna, bearing on her head a huge round basket with which she has left home at three in the morning when the mountains are cold to come to town and peddle her two dozen bananas, her ten mangoes, her twenty sticks of cane which, having sold, she can retrace her steps, not breaking her stride, bearing home a handful of corn meal and two ounces of beans; and next to her, another woman, who has had to walk further, because where she lives there is famine, bearing with her, clotted in rags, her child for whom there is no food, so that both can die in the capital, where there is always hope. The Koda-chromes give way to misery.

But we could see splendor too: capricious and elegant architecture, human beauty and pride, and under the surface of hatred and guilt (for he who is fortunate, does he not feel guilt?), the intelligence that has conquered poverty and ignorance and hunger. We could meet Major B. and hear him say, "Oh, the curse that is on my land, that my people has such an infinite capacity for suffering!" He himself will be outrageously handsome and straight; he will smile a smile that is almost cruel for the varieties of human experience that it has observed. And he is the superior of all but the best of us, more vigorous, more proud, more compassionate, more learned, more wise, more absolute. Or we could go out with his friend Claude D., to see his plantation and have him point out to us a giant kapok tree, a circle of shade half a hundred yards across, saying, "My grandfather planted that tree." The archetype of the squire, dazzling us with attitudes of ease and wealth to which many can only aspire. And yet even he, who has his leisure and the fruits of his forefathers' slavery (at what cost to himself?), still works for his fellow countrymen, teaching farmers only generations from Africa that Nature will give food if only the rocks are wrested from the ground: he could show us two slopes, one that is nothing but rubble, a landslide of aridity, and another that bears rows of cauliflower, beets, potatoes, and young onions, and even, in his imagination, the vine.

Meeting hunger and apathy, meeting vigor and brilliance, we might wonder whether this is the proper place for a holiday. How could we remain blind to the struggle that a man has to wage against nature and fellow man to conquer brutality and ignorance? Or live where history needs, not to be restored, as at Williamsburg, but to be trampled upon, in order that something new may come into existence? Every-where we went, we would see the same disproportion be-tween the way we have chosen to lead our lives, and the way these pople *have* to spend theirs. The Carnival is not mere fun: armorers, plasterers, embroiderers, archivists, painters, panmen work during a year only enough to be able to create their carnival; they make in two days, and then destroy forever, an art in which they find true expression, something we still long for. That monastery that is propped on the side of a volcano, whose monks sing daily, five times, the liturgy that is fifteen centuries old and is the only thing that we possess unchanged from the infancy of our culture, have not placed themselves there for the view, but to take part in the lives of those who inhabit the island.

To be sure, our tourist couple who, by their long acquiesc-ence and silence, are responsible for our American version of *apartheid,* can have no idea of the intensity of feeling through which they stroll, for they have no idea what it is to be, not just a step from being a colony, but just a matter of memory from having been a slave. But we, who are men of heart and sensibility, we know, as much as we can know. And yet we are eunuchs to such societies. We can no more change our skins than our hosts could have in the past. If we make love, we cannot avoid the implications of the past: if we were to accept that we are not master and slave, would *she?* It is the same with the love you could learn for the place you live in.

We would have to add to this the pain we would feel to see ourselves aped in the worst of ourselves, and despised for the best. It is painful to know that it will take even an honest man two generations before he can unlearn the worst that we will teach him.

And our indignities are still not exhausted. For ever-present also is that terrible feeling that our civilization is here being condemned *in toto,* that it has been weighed in some tortured scale, found wanting, and exiled to the periphery of life. The step between a man's knowing that he is bound to inherit the earth because he is one of the down-trodden and oppressed, because numbers are on his side and that awesome thing, divine justice, and his first tasting of that inheritance, is enormous. It opens up a gulf between

him and his past. And those who formerly possessed his inheritance, that is, us, see a pit yawning before us in which
are to be dashed not only our goods, our profits, our status,
our jobs, our lives, and the lives of those we cherish most,
but also that which we prize above all: our image of ourselves, our culture, all that are like us. The fool, the ex-
ploiter, the tourist will go without knowing what it is that
has done them in, full of irrational hatred and rancor, like
a Snopes; but the man of good will and love will also perish,
condemned by the sins of his fathers. And this is suffering.

We will not be asked to help and we will find it hard to
have our capacity for charity limited, just because we are
what we are. In a few decades, our freedom won, our leisure
accumulating, our standard of living raised beyond need,
there will be little else for us to do, except help those whose
lives are not yet equal to our own. To be excluded from that
task is a sentence of exclusion from history.

These are the terrible ironies we face. Our only hope lies
in there being enough of us who, in spite of these ironies
and in spite of the darkness that may engulf us anyway,
will bear witness to the fact that history is not inevitable
and will see that with will and fortitude we might save some
small portion of that which we now consider our inalienable
rights as representatives and bearers of the burden of our
superiority.

THE SIDE OF A BARN

One vote here to blackball those who try to join the club
by clobbering Henry Luce and his magazines. The target is
so big and so easy that it becomes tiresome. Even so it is
misread, and consequent suspicions must arise: (1) that
those firing away really love Luce and are pained at bottom
because the love is not reciprocated with words and pictures;
(2) that the marksmen don't have any genuine understanding
of what is bad about *Time* and *Life*.

This is not to say that, as one academic gentleman recently
wrote of *Life* in *The American Scholar*, "all in all, if anyone
cares, I think the magazine is all right." Such comfortable
old-shoe wisdom is kissing cousin to an entire family of
inane homilies: *Politics stops at the water's edge* (as if that
weren't exactly where it starts nowadays); *What would you
do if YOU were Secretary of State?* (as if anyone with a
shred of principle and sense would have taken the job in the
last eight years); etc., etc.

By now it should be clear that what is wrong with *Life* is

what is wrong with American Life. It undertakes to trivialize experience, it undertakes to erase the qualitative distinction between Robert Frost and Edgar Guest, and the
quantitative distinction between an earthquake and a prom
queen falling on her fanny. As for *Time*, it not only trivializes, it debases and it distorts. It also gives people the feeling
that they know what is going on and therefore don't have to
take the trouble to find out. But once we have said this,
can't we please move on to other matters?

THE UNACKNOWLEDGED CHAMPION OF EVERYTHING

Other Springs have come on strong before. That one where David walked, I've heard, was something quite new in the field. It turned the fields a greener green and flecked the figs of old Gilboa with gold. Yet here in Chicago in the big green middle of a brand-new all-American beginning to everything, I think no Spring before was geared this high.

At the Sunday morning newsstand the papers hadn't been tossed in yet by the news-truck. The newsy hadn't showed up yet. My mind was filled with that Russian dog that had two heads.

That was the reason I was up so early. I knew the *Tribune* could explain everything. I walked on.

Into a Spring strutting like Marilyn Monroe defying traffic lights. That seemed to stand a moment to one side as if listening to someone like June Christy singing about how it's really Spring that hangs her up the most, and you think that must be as fine as any girl can sound. Till Spring herself comes on with lyrics of her own, making the lyrics up as she goes along. A Spring that tops the very best, then tops herself and, breaking off, announces, to all young men from everywhere, that there is a garden where smörgasbord grows from rye bread trees, the Garden Where All Things Are Possible. And all young men are invited to help themselves, and all is free: *Ält är möltig i garden hänger smörgasbord frän ri bröt träden.*

A Spring, that is to say, telling all young men all things are possible. That if you are a young man from Stockholm with a right hand too fast to follow, and the reason you do not use it against sparring partners is that it has such awful power it will take a man's head off five inches below his shoulders and snap it like a twig and all of that, then somewhere in the room is a reporter who, for one fleeting moment thinks—*ält är möltig*—all is possible—and you've sown a seed in the climate of belief. All that then remains to be done is to write a round-robin letter to sports editors and sign yourself: The Unacknowledged Champion of Everything and let the rest to Spring.

"All right, but what about the dog?" I thought I heard someone call, but when I looked around there was nothing but a used-car lot with this year's models already awake and last year's still drowsing about. A cherry-colored pennon above them waved me a cherry-colored good morning.

A morning to bring small Lakeshore poets running, each to speak his winter piece on *Spring O Spring*. Who can sound the most like the way that Mr. Thomas used to sound, that must be the game.

Between the sidewalk and the street a narrow streak of city grass grew so green one breath would breathe it into fire. Would Joseph Rostenkowski, Ward Committeeman, approve a Spring that left things growing in the street? I wondered. Yet it really wasn't so much a Ward Committeeman's Spring as it was a State's Attorney's, a Benjamin Adamowski Spring, and that's the very dandiest kind because it knows where Spring is legally entitled to grow and where it is not.

"It is my proud privilege and special pleasure to announce that the State's Attorney's Office has arranged for Spring to arrive four days early to both sides of W. Division Street. Eastbound traffic will be rerouted past students crossing at St. John's High School. So will westbound traffic as students must not be run down from either direction. Courtesy fees in payment of violation of traffic regulation are not payable on the street, but officers will carry even change just in case. It's the proud privilege and special pleasure of this office to announce that tickets to Riverview Park are now available on a bipartisan basis to well-behaved children under twelve at Wieboldt's well-behaved department store. Sometimes I think a streak of common grass burning between sidewalk and street is a harder thing to understand than a dog with another dog's head growing out of its neck.

Once a candidate for local office offered a hundred dollars as first prize for a poem about Chicago. A hundred dollars was a lot of money then as now, so I sent in a poem about Chicago being freight-handler and hog-butcher to the world and how freight-cars roll in here all night on little cat feet. And signed it "Edna St. Vincent Millay" in order to make a good impression.

I should have signed it "Edna St. Vincent Adamowski" or maybe "Big Joe Rusty Rostenkowski" because I didn't win. The poem that took the hundred began

> Chicago is a stallion wild
> Windstretched and untamed—

I know that doesn't seem real great on paper, but just you try saying it out loud in a whiskey-tavern. You'll find, as we of the Poetry Trade like to put it, that it "gains momentum."

We of the Poetry Trade know how to say a thing to keep the layman in his place. You have to keep the layman in place in any line. "Give a layman a finger," is another we say, "and he'll take the whole hand."

"It's true as Proust" is still another—but this one has to be sort of dropped with an indifferent, even a careless air. I dropped it like that in front of a bartender once—"true as Proust"—just like that—and before I knew it he had drawn me two Pabsts. He was *all* layman.

I tried the bit about Chicago is stallion wild on him, but he didn't even draw a Pabst that time. He just stood there. So I pressed him about did he think Chicago really was a stallion wild. But all he did was keep standing. So I pressed him harder and finally he said, "It's big as Whitman." Then he started that just standing there again. I think he may have been an impostor.

Very few bartenders will order you to leave a place no matter how hard you press them. Sometimes I think they're all impostors.

Another time someone asked a visiting poet what *he* thought about Chicago and the way this fellow put it was, "Death is a message that was never sent." It was Bill Saroyan who first said that, in 1933, only when he said it he laughed so you would know he wasn't just trying to put you on. A friend of the visiting poet stepped up then and said it would be all right with him if someone happened to ask what *he* thought about Chicago. And after he'd been pressed like that he said he thought the same thing about Chicago as he thought everything else, and that was simply, "MEOW!" And he said this "MEOW!" in such a wonderful lifelike way that everyone understood what he had in mind. He thought he was a cat, that was all. We were finally getting somewhere.

But a fellow who was a personal friend of the fellow who was the visiting poet's only friend, came up and said he wanted to start all over, because *he* had the *real* solution.

"Chicago is a *rose*," he said before anyone could stop him, and there we were, right back where we'd started. The fellow had throwed the whole game away on one bad pitch.

For myself I simply couldn't stop thinking about that damned Russian dog. Had the Russians beaten us to it again? Could it mean there was a leak in The American College of Surgeons? How could anyone be

absolutely sure that Morris Fishbein might not still
have relatives in Russia? How, in fact, could anyone
be sure of anything? What was there to stop the
Russians from teaching the top dog to sing, "I Ain't
Got No Body" and thus turn a purely scientific
experiment into a grisly prank? To come down to it,
I realized I myself didn't even know which head I
was thinking about. I really needed a *Tribune* badly.

The Augusta Bakery was still closed, but it was
giving away free smells. You have to go around the
alley where they load the morning delivery trucks to
get one, but you can have all you want so long as you
don't get in the way of the man carrying bread
trays. I picked old-country-rye with seeds to smell
first, even though I hadn't yet had orange juice. This
is a very heavy whiff to hit a person's stomach with
no warning, but I was hungry. Next I tried egg-
bread, plain, but they hadn't used enough eggs.
After that I had a French do-nut, the light kind
without frosting. I didn't hang around for pineapple
cheese sweet rolls because something began to get
me in my middle, like that June Christy coming on
about it being Spring that hangs her up the most
again, and that is exactly what was doing it: Spring
was coming on again like Spring. I walked on.

Into a Spring of old-time church-chimes, old
clocks ticking remembrances of things people used
to say and sing they don't say or sing any more. I
remembered a fellow used to come on between strip
acts at the old Rialto. He weighed in around ninety
pounds and wore a bright orange tie that hung past
his knees and his face was so little and pale behind
it that it made the business of being a man something very comical in itself. The song he sang best
was "O Why Did I Pick a Lemon in the Garden of
Love Where Only Peaches Grow?" His name was
Kenny Brenna and if it wasn't for me both his name
and the song would be lost to posterity.

A big green trolly-bus came racing past with no
one inside it but the driver, and he looked as if it
were driving him. Somehow that reminded me of
somebody else and who it reminded me of was a

Rush Street traffic cop with the idea he is some sort
of EXTRA-ADDED ATTRACTION in the world, so
that one night, just to get onstage, he pulled a gun
on a night-club owner and chased the man across
his own stage with a full house watching, in and out
and around the tables and out the back door onto
Wabash. The owner had been guilty of a serious
traffic violation, he explained; so he got to keep his
gun.

Some extra-added attraction. I don't think I'll so
much as mention him to posterity.

I may mention Ruffy Silverstein, when he wres-
tled at the Marigold and the extra-added attraction
was lady wrestlers. I thought of some Spring whose
bright returning might even bring, to the Coliseum
again, eighty scheduled rounds of boxing featuring
a new West Coast sensation as yet unnamed but
strongly suspected of being Art Aragon.

Some Spring that smells of egg-bread, plain, but
short two eggs per loaf. Of Lakeshore poets, speaking winter pieces, but short two poems per poet. A
Spring of lady wrestlers, short of nothing. Simply
leaping.

Turning off Ashland onto Cortez I saw one Puerto
Rican sitting on top of a Keep-Our-City-Clean box
far from Puerto Rico. He wore a red shirt open at
the throat, top of the cream-colored trousers fresh
from the creamers, and was combing his hair as if he
had just killed somebody on North Clark. When
he saw me coming he replaced the comb and began
to riffle a deck of cards.

"Come to me here you," he ordered as I passed,
"couple fast hands black-jack, just me and you."
The riffle sounded just a little heavy, like a deck with
one extra card. My guess was that it was a queen.
The Polish boys who used to deal seconds around
here never used a queen. The card you had to watch
out for with them was the jack. Don't ask me why.
If I knew why Porkies prefer a queen and Polskies a
jack I'd know about two-headed dogs too. The whole
thing was explained in the *Trib*, but I missed the
issue. I simply have no luck, no luck at all.

"Let me just talk to you," the dealer asked, but I
kept passing, for I knew now who he was. Just plain
old Bill Saroyan still trying to get up his taxes,
nobody else.

If someone has been killed on North Clark it
wasn't me. If the government can get taxes out of
Saroyan, I'll pay mine too.

For I know a Spring that comes on fiercely toot-
ling, red-white-blue and whirlabell, a small girl on
a Fourth-of-July tricycle with flags tied to the
wheels, who leaves her laughter trailing like a
confetti-colored pennant down the long block behind
her.

I know yet another Spring that walks in handsewn
jeans, and rain-gray shirt and cap pulled low, below
the wrack of prison noon: whose lips ask politely
without moving, "Kindly hold this for me," and
walks on never glancing back to where the taped
blade plunged five polite inches in, the paid informer
lies.

And once I saw a Spring of lonesome jacks played
by a girl in a pool of light at the end of a third-floor
hall where no one comes all day. Crosslegged, ball
and jacks, she made up a third-floor Spring as she
went along, just for girls who live behind numbered
doors in halls where no one comes to visit. As if she
felt that the bright noontime city behind her might
stay at noon, and never slowly darken, if she could
find a magic saying to say with ball and jacks. Yet
the city behind her was already darkening fast.

Near the corner of Chicago Avenue and Wolcott
two walls squeezed out on an old unblown bum, one
who had been squeezed between many old walls—
barracks, flophouse, barroom, and cell—that are
made to squeeze men in. This one had been squeezed
between walls where old bricks sweat and slowly
drip, in a cold, uncaring sweat. He came toward me
now with one sleeve slowly squeezing the other and
both elbows squeezing his middle. He had to hold
his head bent a bit forward because something unseen kept squeezing his neck. His cheekbones were
ground in a heavy vise that only a shot of Old Still-

born could loosen. This was the vised man Time and
The Goat had caught between them. When Time and
The Goat begin to press there is nothing on earth
can help a man but Old Stillborn. He held out a card
old brown beggary had begotten. I put it to my eyes
and let the words squeeze themselves to me:

```
DONT   WORRY
DONT   HURRY
BETTER      TO
BE  LATE   TO
THE   GOLDEN
GATE    THAN
ARRIVE      IN
HELL ON TIME
```

Well, what do you know—a philosopher of alleys,
a Ph.D. *A., literally.* He wanted a nickel for his card
so I gave it to him. But after he had been paid and
I walked away, he followed and tugged at my sleeve
furtively, but with determination. He wanted his
card back.

I wouldn't let it go till I saw my nickel. But no—
he hadn't sold me the card at all. He had only sold
me the philosophy on it. If I gave him a dime, he
explained, I could keep both the philosophy and the
card as well.

Now I saw this wasn't just a simply old cross-alley
philosopher with a bottle of Mogen David on one hip
and a pint of Virginia Dare on the other. This was
a real Mortimer Adler of alleys, this was the King-
fish. This bird wasn't giving his nice philosophy
away, he was in *business.*

"Why don't you get the cards made up into sets
of fifty-four and get a desk?" I asked him. "You
wouldn't need an office so long as the weather is so
fine."

He shook his head sadly, and leaned toward me,
whispering some ultimate sadness—*God—he had no
degree.*

I drew back in revulsion. I don't mind a man who
hasn't bathed in months, whose flesh is crawling with
flophouse vermin, whose breath is fermented and
whose eyes are dying. But a man without a degree
makes me sick. I gave him the dime before the

price went up and walked disdainfully away. He was nothing but a bum after all.

Passing the used-car lot again, this year's models looked brighter than ever, but last year's were still drowsing. The cherry-colored pennon that had waved to me had itself gone back on the nod, folded over upon itself above a 1956 Chevvy. A *Tribune* truck sped past and I broke into a run, still clutching my card, because I wanted to be the very first to read what they had thought up in the Tribune Tower the night before.

A small girl was sitting on the stand in a new print frock with a green balloon tethered to her hand.

"Has someone forgotten you, honey?" I asked her. She studied me thoughtfully.

"Where *you* been all night?" she wanted to know.

The way she put that made me think for a moment I might be up against a midget—but what would a midget be doing holding a green balloon?

"You *might* pick up the morning papers," she suggested in that tone so near to scorn. "Or *am* I asking too much?"

Chicago isn't the best town in the world to be seen conversing with an unaccompanied child, and there have been so many laws passed against crime in general lately that I might not even have a defense in pleading that my accuser was a fifty-six-year-old midget. There might be something about talking to unaccompanied midgets. I am all for law and order on Sunday morning, so I put the papers beside her without unbinding them, thinking that might be interpreted later as a ruse to gain time. I left with nothing to read but a small dirty card saying, Don't worry, don't hurry, it's better to be late to the golden gate, and all of that.

By the time I reached the loft I live in I had begun to doubt whether Chicago was really a stallion wild after all. I was sure it's no damned rose. I doubt it's even a rose that says "MEOW!" although that seems to be nearer than thinking of it as a cat that smells like a rose.

What it's really closer to being is just an endless stretch of crisscrossing streets where men from everywhere have come to see how close they can come to killing one another without losing a customer and still stay out of jail.

That's all very well, you may agree or not—but what about the dog?

What dog?

The dog you said, you started to tell us something we never heard before about a dog that had two heads.

It is my proud privilege and special pleasure to announce that Americans need have no fear that Russia may surpass us in creating monsters never before seen in the air above, the earth below, or in the vasty deeps of the ocean sea. By working in twenty-four hour shifts around the clock a team of American scientists have succeeded in producing an Arkansas jackass with a living human head reproduced on its upper right hip.

The head itself is a triumph of American know-how, being a faithful reproduction, formed of cellophane, kapok, and unpaid hotel bills, of a Hollywood film producer wearing his family crest—a salami emblazoned on a director's cap *affrontée*. When publicly exhibited the face will sing "Kookie, Kookie, Lend Me Your Comb." It will then announce a contest, admit that its name is Otto Preminger, and take a profound bow. What true American could ask for more?

Or, as my pert friend of the newsstand inquired, "*Am* I asking too much?"

Am I asking too much of any Sunday-morning balloon-man's Spring in Chicago, that it lift the wishes of all young men in landlocked bars a little, waiting for their lifelong lives to start?

Or raise the hopes of Sunday-morning sidestreet solitaries all over town, to let them drift slowly and low above St. John Cantius and high, then higher, over St. Bonifacius and St. Columbkille, toward that wonderful garden where all things are possible. To all those now merely waiting for rain or bread or

love or peace with a pinch of the salt of magic in it
that will last till the big dark falls.

*Ält är möltig i garden hänger smörgasbord frän
ri bröd träden.*

The garden where all things are possible. And all
is free.

All is free to young men in landlocked bars on
landlocked streets.

In a Spring inviting every young man with a right
hand too fast to follow to be the Unacknowledged
Champion of Everything.

Friendship

I

Jean Kernevel was a man of fifty, big, well-built,
but with a bad heart. His friends had long been
anxiously noting his leaden complexion, his ink-blue
lips, his yellow eyes, and on his face that grave look
men have who know they are under sentence of
death. From his look, one knew he was thinking:
"Perhaps in a month, perhaps in two, but surely
soon."

A bachelor, he lived at the edge of town in a room
he had furnished with his share of his parents'
legacy—an oaken bed, a round table, a cupboard
with two doors, and a pinewood chest of drawers.
The rest of the furniture, three cane chairs and an
armchair, he had picked up secondhand.

His brother Léon, three years his senior, had
gone to live in Paris after his military service. He
had married there and never come back to his own
part of the world. It had taken a war for the two
brothers to see each other again and for Jean to meet

his sister-in-law and his nephews. . . . His sister had married late and remained childless; on learning that her husband had been killed at Verdun, she had gone mad, and since that time had been shut away at the *Incurables*. For Jean Kernevel, this was a grief of which he never spoke, not even to his old friend Fortuné Le Brix.

Next to Jean Kernevel, Fortuné Le Brix seemed small. Kernevel was a head higher than he. Nonetheless, Le Brix was a vigorous man, well set on his legs, and had never known a day's illness. He had abundant red hair, a sanguine complexion, cheeks crisscrossed with tiny violet veins, a strong mustache, and hands like shovels. A bullet wound received at the Somme had left him with a long scar on his left temple; his eye was a little pulled in that direction, which made it look as though he were squinting.

They were both the same age and had hardly been separated since their school days. They had been apprentices together; they had gone off touring together; and before the war they had worked together for the same employers. The war had parted them but a few weeks, after Le Brix's wound and evacuation, and they were soon side by side in the trenches again.

Back home, they had started a small plaster, lime, and cement business with a young and recently married friend, Dagorne. Good workers, all three of them, they had quickly made their mark and earned a good living.

It was Kernevel who managed the business. He had good sense and solidity. He could write a letter and handle accounts; he did not drink and never lost his temper. Dagorne was not without education either, but he was too young to carry authority. As for Le Brix: "Work," he would say, "any amount of work, by God! There's not a son of a bitch in the whole area knows stairs better than I do! But as for writing . . . that's no go! Every man to his own job and let's get on with it!"

In spite of his illness, Jean Kernevel had not

stopped working. When he had no suppliers or clients to call on, he arrived on the job at the same time as the others, and left at the same time, too. But his work got done slowly, and during the day he occasionally rested.

When Le Brix saw him lay down his trowel without saying a word and saw him get down off the scaffolding and lie down in a corner on some sacks, he made a face and thought: "Old Kernevel's flagging. Lose him and lose all. The business'll be done for!" Meanwhile business went on.

They were offered the rough-casting and plastering of a little house being built five kilometers from town. The job was good and the road there easy. A few minutes away was the White Pigeon, where they could catch a bite. A stream flowed nearby, and Dagorne, a born poacher, immediately started talking about laying down nets.

Kernevel figured they had three solid weeks of work, which would take them to the end of September. Then the bad weather could come. They would go back to town and do work indoors. They were not afraid of being unemployed.

The job progressed. The weather stayed fine. At the end of work one Saturday evening, Le Brix had climbed up the scaffolding, as he always did before leaving, to make sure that nothing had been left behind. Kernevel was changing below. Dagorne was already on his way home. He lived out of town and on Saturdays he left an hour early. He arranged it so that he could catch up during the week.

His rounds done, Le Brix came back down into the yard. He was humming a dance-tune and keeping time by nodding his head. He was pleased to be going home, to stop and wet his whistle at the White Pigeon and tomorrow to be spending the afternoon at the Velodrome. Le Brix liked sports, bicycle races most of all. As it happened, tomorrow was a championship race. Bicycle aces had come from Paris.

As he came around a corner of the house, he suddenly stopped humming. At the end of the yard,

Kernevel was sitting on some thick planks, his head in his hands. He was looking at the ground through his legs without moving. "Could he be worse?" Le Brix asked himself.

"Well, old man?" he asked, coming nearer. "Something not going right?"

Without raising his head Kernevel replied, "Not right at all, Fortuné."

"Where's it hurt?"

"It doesn't hurt," Kernevel said. "It's the weakness. My legs won't hold me up."

Kernevel was doubled over, his cap askew, his lips parted, like a man under the weather. His bike was next to him. On the handlebars he had tied his white overalls, rolled up into a package. His breath came heavily.

"Wouldn't you like to lie down?" asked Le Brix. "You could use your overalls as a pillow. Lie down and it'll blow over."

Kernevel shook his head and Le Brix crossed his arms. "A fine fix," he said to himself. "Here I am all alone with a sick man. And how do I get him home?" He looked around, as though hoping for help. But the landscape was empty. The nearest house was the White Pigeon.

"A good slug of rum's what you need," he said. "I'll just hop over to the White Pigeon."

"Wait! Stop, Fortuné! Don't go!" Kernevel cried out. His voice was so weak and worried that Le Brix, who had already taken a few steps, turned half around.

Heavily, Kernevel looked for his handkerchief in the pocket of his jacket. He could not quite bring it up to his brow and Le Brix only just had time to sit down next to him and catch him in his arms. "Good God almighty!" he thought. "It's the real thing! Is he going to die on me?" He took the handkerchief from Kernevel's hand and wiped his friend's brow.

Kernevel indicated that his tie and vest bothered him. Le Brix undid them, but his huge fingers slipped on the buttons and he got angry with himself.

"Don't move," he said. "I'll take care of you."

He sat Kernevel down on the ground, his back against the planks, and put the overalls he untied from the bike under his head. Then he dipped the handkerchief in a tub and moistened his temples.

"That do you good?"

"Yes, Fortuné."

Kernevel passed his hand across his forehead, stretched out his legs, and tried to sit up.

"It'll pass."

"Sure." Le Brix took him up. "I'm going to get you a shot of rum."

He went back into the house to get his bike. "Goddam, goddam, goddam," he swore when he was alone. "It would have to be Saturday night! Dagorne gone an hour ago and five kilometers to home!" Furiously he picked up his bike at arm's length and made as if to throw it far away. "Goddam it to hell! And a flat tire!" He started pumping it in a rage; then he checked his free-wheel and his brakes. "I might have to take him home on my back," he said. After that, he changed, and finally came out into the yard.

Kernevel was standing, ready to leave, his hand on his bike. Le Brix stopped short and shouted: "I suppose you think you're going to bike home!"

"Got to."

"You strong enough?"

Kernevel shrugged his shoulders and repeated, "Got to."

Le Brix knew it was no good contradicting him. He had always obeyed him. It had started early, at children's games; and it had been the same since, even at the front. This obedience was neither servility on his part, nor brutality on Kernevel's: it was born of long custom, of everyday experience, of fraternal friendship. But this time Le Brix wanted to speak his piece.

"What you want to do's crazy, Jean. Wouldn't it be better if I went and got a car?"

"You'll do nothing of the sort," answered Kernevel. "I'll get home on my bike."

He straddled the bicycle and Le Brix said to himself: "How's it all going to end? And if he drops dead on the way?"

Kernevel looked as if he were just learning to ride a bike.

"Ride next to me," Le Brix shouted.

Jean Kernevel did not answer: he gritted his teeth.

II

Fortunately, there wasn't much to it. All they had to do was let themselves be carried into town. The road was easy and as it was after half past seven, there were few cars. Kernevel had taken the lead. He rode hunchbacked, without saying a word. Le Brix could hear him pant. "He's done for," he thought. "But tough. Some character!"

It wasn't the first time Kernevel showed Le Brix this kind of courage. All his life he had shown it. At the front, a calm man—but then the front wasn't the same thing. It was just a matter of waiting. There was no choice. Whereas now, if he had wanted, he could have had a car.

The road crossed the moors. They went by the White Pigeon without stopping. With the night, some clouds rose in the sky. They didn't take the time to light up.

At a turning in the road, the town appeared, with its lights, in the plain. It was high time they got there. When Kernevel got off his bicycle, at his door, he would have fallen to the sidewalk if Le Brix hadn't held him up.

It was an old house, with long windows full of small square panes. The door gave onto a stone staircase: like a railing, a rope hung there, thick as a cable, black and shining, and ending in a knot. With one hand Kernevel clung to this rope; it tightened with a snap.

"Home, Jean," said Le Brix. "I'll give you a hand up to your room. You'll have to lie down."

"It's my bed I need, all right."

He stopped at every step to catch his breath. Two flights they went up that way; then Kernevel took a key from his pocket. "Here," he said.

The room was in order. The oaken bed with its batiste curtains was covered with a red eiderdown. By the bed were lined up the two chairs and the armchair, and in the middle of the room the round table, with its flowered oilcloth, bore an oil lamp. Kernevel let himself fall into the armchair and Le Brix lit the lamp.

"Poor old Fortuné," said Kernevel, throwing his cap on the bed. "Here I am home. I thought I'd never get here."

"Don't think about it, man. Get to bed now," answered Le Brix.

"Wait. Let me breathe."

He was spent and his hands trembled on his knees where he had placed them.

"When you're in bed," Le Brix said, "I'll go find you something to eat."

"I don't want anything. I want to go to bed and sleep if I can. You ought to go home yourself, Fortuné. You're wife'll be wondering where you are. She'll give you hell."

"Bah! It won't be the first time. I want to see you in bed before I start home."

Kernevel rose from the armchair. He took off his jacket. Le Brix started walking up and down the room.

He had rarely entered it. The last time had been a year ago; he'd helped his friend whitewash the ceiling. The wash had held up well, but the walls needed it badly. Kernevel had hung some chromos. Le Brix looked them over one by one. Then he went over to the chest of drawers on which Kernevel had arranged some photographs, framed in red velvet: of his father and his mother, of his brother as a soldier, and of his sister on her twentieth birthday. Le Brix greatly respected the orderliness that reigned in the room. It was Kernevel himself who took care of it every morning as his coffee was warming upon the wood-alcohol stove.

Le Brix heard a groan and turned around. Kernevel had bent over to undo his shoelaces and now had straightened up. "I can't . . ."

"You see!" Le Brix shouted. "Don't push it. Don't move; let me handle this."

He kneeled down and untied the laces on the great hobnailed boots Kernevel wore. The leather was reddened all over with mortar. Then he helped him off with his corduroys and his jersey and said: "Think you can get into bed alone?"

He pulled back the blanket and Kernevel got in without a word. But once he lay stretched out with his head on the pillow, tears filled his eyes.

"What's that for?" said Le Brix. "What's got into you? Come on, man: you mustn't worry. Don't think, sleep. I'll be back in the morning. You need anything?"

"Nothing, Fortuné."

"Tomorrow then, and sleep."

He shook his head and left. "There's a man who worries too much," he said to himself, shrugging his shoulders.

It was night. Le Brix lit his lamp and jumped onto his bike.

His wife was waiting for him. She was a short woman of forty, thin, dark, and shrill, but goodhearted and a worker. Her hair was dressed in the old way, with a chignon and a puff. She was wellknown in the district: Marie, Le Brix's wife, with her two tiny black eyes always on the lookout. She was a charwoman.

When Le Brix opened the door, she was at the stove, watching over the stew. She turned around, ladle in hand. No sooner had he taken a step into the room than she began swearing at him.

"There you are, you drunkard!" she shouted. "And where were you? Here I was eating myself up waiting for you!"

She threatened him with the ladle. He did not answer, put his tools down on a chair, and sat down at the table in front of his plate.

The room was low-ceilinged but huge. They had lived there all the twenty-five years of their marriage. They were happy in this huge room that had seemed so empty when they had set up house, when all the furniture they had in the world was a bed, a table, and a charcoal stove. But day by day the room had been furnished. One day they bought a stove, which they put near the bed to keep them warm in winter. Another day, a cupboard; then chairs and utensils. Today they were so numerous that no one knew where they had been obtained, or how. There were boxes filled with God knows what, rusty tacks and tools. Against a whitewashed wall stood the black staff of a flag in its sheath: the red flag, stored with Fortuné Le Brix since the town had closed down the Labor Exchange.

Marie turned down the lamp that had flared up. "Here it is so late I can't see a thing," she said. "Oh, you wretch!"

He played deaf. And she went on insulting him. All afternoon she had counted on going to the movies that night, as sometimes happened on Saturdays. The idea had stuck in her head. It was a thought, a wish, and she'd enjoyed a private joke about it, for there was little likelihood that she would have any other kind of desires. On that subject she was firm. She had no children and she would not have any. It was too late and she no longer even regretted it as she once had, back in the days when she had quarreled about it with Fortuné, who was, notwithstanding, a warm-blooded man.

With the movies in mind she had hurried through her work and made the stew. Then eight o'clock had struck and no husband! Eight-thirty and still no one. And now he came in, after nine o'clock!

"Ah, so help me, you drunkard!"

Finally, he had enough of it. He struck a great blow on the table with his fist and got up. "Goddam it!" he said. "Now you're going to shut up, Marie."

From time to time, if she got too shrill, he would

hit her one. Then she would quiet down right away.

"Look out, woman," he said, his hand raised. "Just bring the soup."

She looked him over carefully. No, he was not drunk. But his looks indicated that something serious had happened. She had seen those eyes before, when there had been an accident. Her anger dissipated. She put the soup pot on the table in front of Le Brix and took the bread and a bottle of red wine out of the sideboard.

"What's wrong?" she asked.

"Wrong, Marie," he answered, "is that Kernevel's done for. Do you understand that?"

She opened her mouth, but said nothing. Le Brix gulped his soup down noisily.

"Well," he said between two mouthfuls, "eat your soup."

"What kind of a story's that? Jean Kernevel?"

"That's what I said."

The whole meal long they exchanged not a word. When Le Brix finished, he wiped his knife, pushed aside his plate, and told how Jean Kernevel had had an attack on the job.

"He insisted on coming home on his bike, but I had to put him to bed."

Elbows on the table, Marie listened. She did not want to believe her husband. She wanted details and more details.

"It's just not possible," she said.

"And," Le Brix concluded, "just on a Saturday night, Dagorne gone home, damn it!"

"And . . . ?" she asked. "And the business?"

Furious, he answered: "Business, there's no question of business right now, Marie."

He rolled himself a cigarette, drank his coffee, walked around the room a while, and went to bed while Marie washed the dishes.

III

Le Brix woke up at daylight. Marie was still dozing. "And Jean?" he said to himself. "I wonder how he's feeling."

He got up gently, not to wake up his wife and dressed. From the cupboard he took a clean cloth, a piece of Marseilles soap, and went out.

The street was fresh and empty. He made good time to the wash-house: a covered wash-house, built along the road at the end of town and fed by a fountain whose water was perpetually pure. Sunday mornings, like many of his friends in the district, Le Brix went there to perform his ablutions.

In the wash-house, he took off his shirt. Naked to the belt, he shivered. Suddenly, kneeling on the ledge, he ducked his head into the water; nothing like it, he was wont to say, to wake up a man. He rose dripping, his eyelids burning, and groped for the soap he had put down next to him. Then he rubbed his neck, his arms, and his hair, in which lumps of plaster and lime stubbornly refused to budge. He tore them out with rage, grimacing with pain, and urged himself on with jokes and oaths. Finally, he rinsed and dried himself off, snorting.

Only Sundays was he able to undertake what he called the "great wash." The other days, eye on the clock, he barely had time to pass the tip of a wet cloth across his eyes.

Once ready, he strode out into the fields. After a great wash he always took a walk, to "react." Sometimes he went as far as the Mare Melée, and breakfasted there with a great bowl of black coffee and a slice of buttered bread. Then he would walk back slowly, smoking a cigarette. This time he did not go so far.

A wind blew right along the ground. The earth was wet. On the edge of a vale, he stopped momentarily; the spot pleased him. From there he could see a whole stretch of country, and rising from it, the belfries of two villages, and farther on, the gray line of the shore and the sea. . . . He started back. The walk had warmed his blood. He was hungry.

Marie was up, dressed in a jacket and a petticoat of thick white wool with red stripes. Her hair was carelessly braided and struck her on the back every time she moved. Breakfast was ready.

"Here," she said. "It'll do you good if you've been out walking."

"I took a short one. I'm afraid it's not going to clear up; it looks like rain later. Still, I should see Dagorne later."

"You certainly should," she said.

He swallowed down his milk and bread; then he went out and fed his rabbits. Behind the house, at one end of the yard, he had a little corner of his own. When he had fed his animals, he shaved. Then he fetched his Sunday clothes, smoked a cigarette, and polished his shoes, one foot on a chair.

"I'm going to Jean," he said.

"Don't go empty-handed," she answered. "Here's a pot with some broth in it. Warm him up. And tell him I'm making some more, fresh, and he'll get it tomorrow."

"All right."

His hand was on the door.

"And buy him something on the way. Some oranges if you like. And say 'hello' to him from me."

He nodded his head and left.

Ordinarily, Sunday mornings passed like the wind. He went lazily from inn to inn. There was no question of inns today. He went straight to Kernevel's, walking as he did on his way to work. As he walked, he kept on repeating to himself: "How'll I find him? I wonder if he's had any sleep." The more he thought about Kernevel, the more worried he grew. "Poor fellow," he thought, "and only fifty years old!"

IV

Kernevel was not asleep. The morning light bothered him and he shut his eyes. But he was not strong enough to get up and close the shutters.

It had been a bad night. After Le Brix had gone, he had grown drowsy; then, at midnight, he had been awakened by a pain in his side. He had been unable to get to sleep again: until daybreak he had counted the hours.

Since he had fallen ill, Kernevel had been through

some bad moments, but he had taken even the worst of them without giving in. But this one was not like the others. "No," he said, "this time I've really had it. But if it lasts, what will the others do? How'll they get along?"

Thinking made him worry more. To finish the job they had in hand, three fit men putting in their ten hours a day were not too many. Now there would be only two and Dagorne would have to lose time seeing customers. "Will he be able to stand up to them?" Kernevel asked himself. "What a shame, it was going so well!"

He did not try to hide the truth about his condition from himself. He felt that if his illness dragged on he would have to go to the hospital. He was afraid of the hospital. His father had died there, and after his father, his mother. He told himself that when he went in his turn, it would be to die. It was not the fear of dying that made him afraid of the hospital. The fear of death he fought as well as he could; but he did not want to be abandoned.

It was a dark night. The noises outside had all ceased. Kernevel was alone in his bed, thinking. "Bah!" he said. "Sick men's fancies!" And to drive them away, he wanted to think some more about the business, about the work that couldn't wait, about his accounts.

He had his own way of running the business and there were lots of little details that he settled without telling his companions; they were hardly worth talking about. But suddenly, he was overtaken by scruples. His accounts were up to the moment and well-kept, but nevertheless there were some things that his partners would not understand unless he explained them. And if he should die suddenly, as could happen? And without seeing them again? This thought so tormented him that he turned over and over in his bed, moaning. Once he was gone and they looked at the accounts, they might think that he had cheated them of some money. He would not be able to defend himself, or show them that he had always been honest. All feverish as he was, he would have liked to get up and take out his notebooks; but he could not. "Ah," he thought, "I've really had it this time, really had it." At the same time, he was angry at himself for thinking his friends capable of such an accusation. But no matter how much he repeated to himself that such an idea would never enter Le Brix's or Dagorne's head, he could not rid himself of his anxiety. "As soon as I see them again," he promised himself, "I'll talk to them about the accounts." This thought calmed him a little.

He heard the street wake up, with joy. People called from one window to another. A man began singing at the top of his voice. Water thrown from a window fell into the street in one great splash. These were Sunday noises, so different from weekday ones. On weekdays, there was not much singing to be heard. Steps on the stairs told him that his neighbors were going out on a trip and were hurrying to catch the first train.

The day rose; it filled the room. Kernevel was looking at the light on the walls when Le Brix entered.

"I was waiting for you," he said. "I knew you'd get here early."

"Damn right!" answered Le Brix, putting the pot down on the table. "Did you get some sleep?"

"Not much. I woke up at the stroke of midnight with a pain in my side."

He was lying flat on his back and spoke without moving his head. His eyes were yellow, his complexion mud-colored and his lips puffed. "He's not getting any stronger," Le Brix said to himself. "Got to see a doctor, there's no getting around it." Nor would it be an easy matter. Kernevel wouldn't want to hear talk of a doctor . . . and yet!

"What's in the pot?"

"Some broth from Marie. You'll have some fresh tomorrow. She's making some. Where's your stove?"

"Open the cupboard. Right in front of you. But I'm not hungry."

"Got to eat."

Le Brix poured the soup into the pot in which

Kernevel heated his morning coffee and lit the stove. Then he sat down by the edge of the bed and stayed there, his great, bare, clay-colored hands resting on his knees. He chewed on a cigarette, wondering how he could bring up the question of a doctor. Finally he said:

"Listen Jean, old man, I don't mean to say that you look worse. On the contrary, you look better than last night. But for the sake of your conscience, don't you think I ought to go get the doctor for you? Old Houdan lives nearby, you know that. And he's a good guy. What do you say?"

"It'd be a waste of time, Fortuné."

"Bah! It'd take a weight off your mind."

"I don't need a doctor. I know what I've got."

There was nothing Le Brix could answer. He knew that unfortunately doctors were pretty much alike; they served to kill you a little quicker, but that was all. He wanted no part of them himself; no more than he wanted a priest. On that score he'd already made his wishes known to Marie. But it wasn't his time yet, and regardless of the poor opinion he had of doctors in general, he was ready to admit that old Houdan was a fine fellow and devoted to his patients.

"Damn it, Jean, you're a stubborn character!"

"That's beside the point. The fact is, old Houdan can't do anything."

"Where does it hurt?"

"Nowhere."

The same question, the same answer as last night. The idea that Kernevel was not suffering disconcerted Le Brix. What could the matter be that he should be so sick and yet feel no pain? Nothing above board, that was sure! Wouldn't it be better to suffer one good blow and have it all done with?

The soup was steaming on the stove.

"Sit up, Jean."

Kernevel sat up painfully in bed. He took the bowl Le Brix handed him with both hands and swallowed a gulp. Le Brix, arms dangling, watched his every move with an affectionate air.

"All of it, bottoms up! That's where the best of it is!"

"Easy, friend, little by little," Kernevel replied. He put the bowl down on the night-table.

"Didn't you yourself tell me you had a pain in your side?"

"Yes, but it went away. I feel weak, that's all. You'll have to get along without me tomorrow."

Le Brix thought: "He's done for."

"I brought you some oranges," he said.

Kernevel jumped. During his father's last days, they had brought him oranges to the hospital. "Am I sicker than I think?" he asked himself. Le Brix took the oranges out of his pocket. There were a half-dozen of them.

"For when you wake up at night and feel thirsty."

"Thanks, Fortuné, you're a good man."

But his voice was so sad that Fortuné, crossing his arms, protested.

"What's the matter with you? Don't drop out now, Jean. Don't go soft on me now, goddam it! What's the point of turning sad on me all of a sudden? I'll be damned! Do I have to put up with stuff like that?" he said furiously.

Kernevel shook his head to indicate his indifference and said: "Bring me my accounts. They're in the cupboard, in the bottom drawer."

In the drawer Le Brix found two little notebooks with red edges, bound in gray cloth and kept shut with elastic bands. He handed them to Kernevel.

"These the ones you mean?"

"Yes, take them with you. Give them to Dagorne and tell him to come and see me. I've got some things to explain to him. Promise?"

"Count on it," Le Brix answered, stuffing the notebooks in his pocket. "I'll go and see Dagorne this afternoon."

"Good. Thanks, Fortuné. Now leave me. I think I'll rest."

V

Dagorne lived in a village on the Paris road. It
was a good four-kilometer ride. After lunching, Le
Brix took his siesta. He woke up on the stroke of
half-past two and took a quick look at the weather.
The sky had cleared. "Good," he said, "I'll walk
there."

And he left.

The road went right past the Velodrome. He heard
people cheering the racers and climbed up an em-
bankment, trying to see them. But he could see
nothing and he set off again.

He found Dagorne playing bowls in the village
square, as he had expected.

Dagorne was a jovial man, but "staid." He was
twenty-six and just beginning to fill out. High-
colored and bright-eyed, his look of health was a joy
to see. In five years of marriage he had produced
two girls and a boy; they were expecting a fourth.

Seeing Le Brix, he stopped bowling and came up
to him.

"A miracle," he said, drying his hands on his
pants. "You mean to say you're not at the races?"

"I don't give a good damn about racing," Le Brix
answered. "Come on over here."

He dragged Dagorne along with him.

"Now," he said, "this is the story: Kernevel's had
it."

The two men stopped and looked at each other.
Then they took a few more steps. The bowlers were
calling after Dagorne: it was his turn to bowl. He
made signs to them that he was not going back to
the game.

"Let's go to my place," he said.

He did not live in the village itself, but two hundred meters away, in a little house standing by itself,
built of gray stones and roofed with slate. A path
led up to it, which they went along without saying
a word.

Dagorne's wife stood on the threshold. She had a
baby in her arms. She was a small woman, dressed

all in black, pale and spotty, her hair pulled back
and bound in a net. Her belly was enormous. She
smiled when she saw them.

"You've decided to come and see us," she said.
"Please come in."

She herself went in first and cast a quick eye
about to see that everything was in order. The baby
was asleep; she put it in the crib.

The two men went and sat next to the fire.

Two beds, end to end, took up the back wall of
the room. The parents slept in one, the two
girls in the other. In the middle of the room, right
on the earthen floor, was the table, and in front of
the chimney was the stove, which hissed. Although
the daylight was already growing weak, the copper
on the buffet shone.

"What will you have, Fortuné?" asked Dagorne.

"Nothing, thank you."

"You'll make me feel ashamed. Give us a little
coffee, will you, Angèle?"

She got busy, fetched the cups out of the buffet,
the bread and butter, and put the coffee pot on the
stove. They said nothing.

"What's the matter with you good people?" Angèle
asked. "Nothing wrong, I hope?"

They were startled. Women always seem to
know everything, just by looking.

"Nothing exactly wrong," said Le Brix, "but
nothing good, either."

And Dagorne added: "Old Kernevel's sick."

To herself she said that Kernevel must be really
sick for Le Brix to trouble himself on a Sunday to
tell her husband.

"Ah, poor Kernevel. I thought something bad
would happen, the way his color had gone. And always thinking. It's his heart, I suppose?"

"He feels weak, he says. It doesn't hurt."

"His heart," she said. "That's bad."

They had taken out their knives and Dagorne set
himself to cutting big slices off the round loaf. Angèle
brought the coffee and a bottle of unpressed wine. It
was very pleasant. The smell of the coffee filled the

room. She opened the stove to stoke up the fire and a glow rose to the ceiling.

Le Brix ate with appetite. He was worn out from his walk. He was not used to it and four kilometers at a stretch hurt his legs more than twenty kilometers on a bike. Sitting there and feeling nice and warm and relaxed, drinking down his coffee and sometimes pouring it over his bread, contentment stole over him. Nevertheless, the thought of Kernevel would not quit him.

"It took him all of a sudden," he said. "Last night, on the job. I thought he was gone. But that's a man with will power. You know that, Dagorne? He came back on his bike, by God! I think that finished him off. He looked weak this morning."

They pondered. Angèle sat at a corner of the table and ate without appetite. If old Kernevel died, what would happen to the business? Of course, she felt sorry for the poor devil. It was a shame to see a young man like him, with so much life in him, taken off before his time. But with him gone, they'd never find another like him; and two-man businesses —well, they just don't work. Her husband would go back to working for someone else, like before. They wouldn't die of hunger, but it would be a narrow squeeze. No employer would give him what he now brought home every week. How manage it, with three children to bring up, and soon a fourth?

"Has he seen a doctor?" she asked.

"He won't have anything to do with one," answered Le Brix. "And besides, he's gotten ideas into his head. He cries."

Dagorne shook his head. A bad sign. Sick people are close to their end when they start crying. He'd seen it, often.

"He must feel pretty sick," he said.

"To my way of thinking, Dagorne, he won't pull through."

Le Brix regretted his words. Perhaps they should not have been spoken. The silence that followed embarrassed him, and he broke it:

"He's eating himself up, old man. You go and

see him tomorrow, as soon as you can. He gave me
the accounts. Here . . ."

He drew the two notebooks from his pocket and
put them on the table. Dagorne took them and
turned them around in his fingers. Finally he
shrugged his shoulders and handed them to his wife.

"Here, put them away, in the drawer. It's no
time to be settling accounts, now."

He poured himself a little brandy and offered
some to Le Brix. "A bad sign," he said to himself.
"A man who cries and can't keep up his accounts."

Angèle had come to sit by the crib. Her mind was
still on the same subject.

"If you ask me," Dagorne said, "he's got to be
sent to the doctor. You hear me, Fortuné?"

"That's my idea too," answered Le Brix. "Tomorrow I'll go fetch old Houdan."

Le Brix got up, apologizing for the trouble.
Dagorne accompanied him as far as the village. On
the square, he left him. He was off in another
direction to fetch his two daughters, who had been
picked up in the morning, as on every Sunday, by
a sister-in-law.

VI

Monday morning, Le Brix got up with the sun
and drank down his breakfast while Marie filled a
canteen he had brought back from the trenches with
fresh broth. He slung the canteen over his shoulder
and leaped onto his bike. On his way, he stopped in
at Doctor Houdan's, in spite of the early hour. The
Doctor promised he would be there shortly.

Le Brix found Kernevel awake.

"Well, old man, so you won't sleep," he said. "I've
brought you some fresh broth. I'll make your bed
while it's warming up. You must need it. Get up."

"I give you a lot of trouble," Kernevel said.

"Forget it. We're here to give each other a hand."

Kernevel let his legs slip to the ground and,
leaning on his friend's shoulder, sat down in the
armchair and wrapped himself up in a blanket. Le
Brix gathered up the eiderdown, the sheets, and the

pillow and put them on the edge of the open window. He turned over the mattress and beat it flat with his hands. He looked like a baker at his trough. He went backwards and forwards endlessly and the huge nails on his boots sounded sharply on the floor.

"I feel like I'm back in the Army," he said.

"Those were good times, Fortuné."

"Good times, old man. Don't worry. I'll make you a bed you'll feel real fine in."

He stretched the sheets out to eliminate the wrinkles, and he beat the bolster and pillows with great blows. When he had finished, he said: "In with you!"

He helped Kernevel back into bed and made him drink his broth. This time Kernevel drank it to the dregs.

"That's better," said Le Brix. "How do you feel in a freshly made bed?"

"Fine, thanks to your good heart, Fortuné."

"Damn it, man, there's no 'thanks' to it. Just tell me, who would take care of you if I didn't, eh, poor Jean? Right now I'd better empty the pot."

Kernevel shook his head.

"No," he said.

"Why not?"

"Because I don't want you to do latrine duty."

"Why make such a fuss? Goddam it," he swore, "I sure as hell will."

He took the pot and went out to empty it in the latrine in the yard.

When he came back up Dagorne and Doctor Houdan, having met on the stairs, were sitting by the bedside. Without feeling ashamed, Le Brix put the pot back in the night-table.

Houdan was a little old man with sideburns and bifocals. He wore an overcoat with an astrakhan collar. He had put his bowler hat down on the table and was rubbing his hands together, a tic of his, meanwhile firing questions at Kernevel: How long had he been ill? How had this last attack taken place? How was his appetite? Did he get some sleep? Kernevel replied dully, and every time he answered

a question Houdan said: "Yes, very good," nodding
his head. Dagorne and Le Brix watched without
moving. Houdan auscultated Kernevel and when he
got up again he took a notebook out of his pocket
and wrote out a prescription. He said:

"I'm going to give you a powder, which you'll
take morning and evening. But what you need most
of all is rest and no emotional disturbances, no
worries." He took up his hat and made for the door.
"It's a matter of patience," he said. "And if anything happens, send for me."

Le Brix joined him on the stairs.

"Doctor Houdan," he called.

"Ah," said Houdan, anticipating his question.
"He's a very sick man. He'd be better off in the
hospital."

Le Brix had been saying the same thing to himself. A hospital was a hospital, of course; everyone knows what that means. But at least one is
cared for. He asked: "Will he pull through?"

"I don't know," answered the Doctor. "I can't
tell you anything, except that he's very sick; and
above all, that there must be no disturbances."

He went off down the stairs and Le Brix returned to Kernevel.

The visit had tired Kernevel. His hands were
stretched out, open, on the blanket. Le Brix sat
down. After a moment, Kernevel called out:
"Dagorne?"

"Yes."

"Did you bring the accounts?"

"Here," said Dagorne.

"Did you look them over?"

"No."

"Oh," Kernevel said. "You should have. Come
closer, Fortuné. Let's have a look at them together.
They're all in order, you know. . . ."

They didn't know whether to laugh or be furious.

"Damn it, Kernevel," Dagorne broke out, "a fine
thing to bring us so early in the morning! Some
idea! Of course the accounts are in order; catch

me ever going over them after you've done with them."

"I want you to."

Le Brix folded his arms.

"You haven't gone crazy by any chance, have you? If you ever say another word like that . . ."

But Dagorne quieted him down.

"Quiet, Fortuné. If he wants to, let's do it. Here," he said to Kernevel, handing him the notebooks. "Here they are."

Kernevel, notebooks in hand, started explaining to his friends. Here there were so many sacks of lime due. A harness they had made two months ago hadn't been paid for yet. A bill should be sent right away. He had not noted down so many bags of cement bought from a fellow tradesman because he owed them several cart-loads of sand. They should more or less even out. The man would have to be seen and the business settled. He would have gone himself if he hadn't been sick. And there were last month's accounts, too. Everything had to be checked.

Le Brix listened without understanding. He was too angry. Dagorne nodded.

Finally Kernevel shut the notebooks and said: "Everything's in order. You saw that, Dagorne?"

"Yes."

"And you, Fortuné?"

"Sure. You didn't have to make all that fuss about it."

Kernevel looked into Le Brix's eyes. "It's not that I don't have confidence in you," he said, "but I don't want you to have anything to reproach me with."

It was after nine. They went off to work.

VII

Their hearts weren't in their work, and yet they had to get on with it. The quicker they got through with this job, the better it would be for all concerned. With a little money in their pockets, they'd feel safer. They were going to need it. Dagorne thought of his wife, who would be delivered soon:

deliveries didn't come free. They worked until the
very last ray of light, eating lunch on the job so as
not to lose time going to and coming back from the
White Pigeon.

Kernevel was no better. On the contrary. From
day to day he weakened, he ate less, he grew thin.
The nights were particularly bad. The fever kept
him awake.

Every morning at the same time, Le Brix arrived
with his canteen. He made the bed, forced Kernevel
to take his medicine and swallow a little soup. He
emptied the pot. As it happened, Le Brix was somewhat squeamish, a defect of which he was ashamed
and which he hid. No one ever knew that more than
once he had vomited up his breakfast carrying out
the pot. But nothing in the world would have made
him give in, and so long as Kernevel was ill, he
kept it up. He would settle his stomach with a
little glass of rum on his way to work.

Sometimes, in the afternoons, Marie would get to
Kernevel's. She would bring him a brioche, some
fruit, or applesauce between two plates. She would
light him a wood fire in the fireplace. Unfortunately,
she never stopped talking and her shrill voice destroyed Kernevel, happy as he was to see her. He was
a little ashamed and when he could no longer bear
listening to her he would pretend to doze off. Then
she would fall silent and creep off without a sound.

He would stay alone until evening. Le Brix then
came to see him, and sometimes Dagorne. The work
went on in spite of everything, and they would soon
be back in town.

"Don't worry, Kernevel," Dagorne said, "I'll manage."

In fact, he showed himself quite capable of doing
so, and Kernevel stopped worrying about the business. "Once I'm gone," he said to himself, "Dagorne
will run it. They'll find a third man to take my
place."

A week passed this way.

When Sunday came around again, Le Brix shaved
Kernevel. For several days he had been telling him:

"Your beard's grown too much. It makes you look woebegone. You ought to take it off."

His beard had grown thick, right up to under the eyes, and low on his neck. But what did Kernevel care about the state of his beard? Still, he let Le Brix go to it and Le Brix put the water on to heat and meanwhile cracked jokes: Kernevel's beard, he said, he was going to cut just as if Kernevel were some fat businessman! First he washed his friend's face; his movements were awkward and rough. But with the razor itself he showed himself to be more capable. And when it was done, Kernevel passed his hand over his cheek, now smooth, and smiled. It was the first time Le Brix had seen him smile since he had taken to his bed. He was so happy about it that he started rubbing his hands together like old Houdan and said: "Now you look like a human being. But thank God no one saw you an hour ago! What would he have thought?"

There was no doubt he did look better after the shave, but under the beard his cheeks were sunken and hollow. Kernevel wanted a mirror. He examined himself at length and rolled his eyes to see the yellowness in them. He gave the mirror back to Le Brix without a word.

All week long he had waited for Sunday, hoping to have company for a slightly longer visit. And now here was Fortuné, and even his company was a burden. It was without pleasure that he saw Le Brix come back in the afternoon, this time accompanied by Marie, all dressed up in a hat, and Dagorne. He would have liked to be alone. They stayed a long time and he was barely able to pry his lips apart to say anything; at the same time he was angry with himself for seeming so ill-tempered. He wondered why he was suddenly behaving that way.

VIII

After leaving Kernevel, Dagorne was the first who dared to speak.

"He's sinking," he said.

Le Brix spat out his cigarette into the gutter.
"Yes, Dagorne, more's the pity."

"I know he has a sister at the *Incurables,* but
doesn't he also have a brother?"

"Yes," answered Marie, "his brother Léon. He
lives in Paris."

It was late. Each of them said to himself that he
ought to be getting home, but each of them lacked
the strength to quit the others. Le Brix said: "Let's
go have a drink."

They went into an inn. The room was small, stinking, and jammed. They ordered cider. Marie took off
her hat; it was giving her a headache. She wasn't
used to dressing up.

"Don't you think we ought to let him know?"
asked Dagorne.

"His brother?"

"Yes."

Le Brix grimaced. "You really think so, Dagorne?"

"It looks that way."

"A delicate matter," he said.

From his pocket he drew out his tobacco pouch
and his cigarette paper; he passed them to Dagorne.

"It's not really our business," he began again. "I've
thought about it, of course, but so long as Jean
doesn't mention it, we have no business meddling."

"You've got to remember that they quarreled,"
said Marie.

"I don't deny it," Dagorne answered. "They may
well have fallen out for all I know; but a quarrel
then and a quarrel now . . . things have changed."

They drank and then put their mugs down on the
table and looked at each other. Marie pursed her
lips.

"That's not this year's cider," she said.

"You're right, woman. It's hard as hell. The
bastards! Not like the cider we get at the Pigeon,
eh, Dagorne?"

"Not even close," said Dagorne as he wiped his
mouth with the back of his hand. "But to come back
to the brother. If they have something to say to
each other, they ought not to wait too long."

It was true. In a week, Kernevel had greatly deteriorated. The worst was to be expected. Why hide the fact? The first few days, they had hoped, in spite of everything. But when a man can spend a whole evening without letting out two words, what else could you conclude?

"I get your point," Le Brix said. "And perhaps it's a good one. As for us, we do what we can. But it's not the same thing, after all. We're just friends, and family's family. That's the way it is. And me, Dagorne, if I was like him, on the point of kicking off, don't you think I'd be happy to see my brother Adrien again?"

"You've got a brother?"

"Yes. You didn't know? He's ten years younger than I am. You might say I brought him up myself. He took off twenty years ago and no one's ever heard of him since."

"Perhaps he's dead," said Marie.

"What do you know about it?" Le Brix retorted. "You just let your tongue wag too much. To my way of thinking, he's not dead. It just happened that it wasn't in him to write letters, and that's all there is to it. He'll be like my uncle, my father's brother: he'll turn up after forty years. No one expected *him* to turn up! The proof of it is, my mother took him for a tramp."

"Ah," said Dagorne.

"That's no cock-and-bull story, Dagorne; you can ask Marie there. What's the use? That's the way it is with us. When you have to earn your living, there's not much time to think about others. Or rather . . . there is time, we do think about them. But when do you have time to write? No, Marie, I doubt he's dead. It's a hunch I have."

"And when the police came for him, for his twenty-eight days? Where was he?"

"Police!" Le Brix burst out with scorn. "A batch of good-for-nothings! You can tell them . . ."

"And when they came back, about the war, did they find him then?"

"Of course not. But he's a smart fellow. He

thought of a way out. He thinks we're a batch of
pricks for playing along with it."

Excited by his own words, he had raised his voice.

"Don't talk so loud," Marie said. "People are
looking at you."

"I don't give a damn!" he answered. "He's right,
too: we did play along with the war like a bunch of
pricks, and I'll say it again: it's just too bad if it
bothers anyone to hear it! And if Jean Kernevel's
dying right now, you can damn well say it's their
fault. There's a man who was as healthy as I am
before the war. He did his job quietly and he didn't
ask anyone for anything. I'm not saying he was in
seventh heaven, but he managed. Then they came to
fetch him. Why? Me, I tell you it's their fault.
They're a bunch of crooks. When I think of what he
was. . . . And look at him now!"

An old, long-standing anger rose within him.
Whole days went by when he never thought of
these things, days when they were as though forgotten. One has to forget if one is to go on living.
But then other days, the memories came back to him,
and for weeks they would not let him out of their
grip. Nights, he dreamed about the front. He sat up
in bed screaming.

"I thought I was still there," he would say to
Marie. His shouts would have woken her up.

She would calm him as well as she could. "Go to
sleep, go to sleep," she would repeat, "stop bother-
ing us with this war of yours." But he did not dare
go back to sleep for fear of tumbling back into his
nightmare. He would pull his legs out of the bed and
strike his knees with the sharp edge of his hand.
Some clever fellow in the hospital had shown him
how to get rid of nightmares that way. Nightmares,
he said, came from poor circulation, and all you had
to do to restore it was hit yourself on the knee.

"You'll have another one of your dreams," Marie
said, seeing her husband getting excited. "You think
Kernevel got what he's got at the front, eh? He
wasn't sick when he came back."

Le Brix made a move as though to hit her. "That's

women for you," he said. "So, he didn't get it at
the front? I suppose you think the front cured him?"

She fell silent, fearing his temper. She wanted to
go home. She said it was late, but Le Brix refused
to go and ordered another round, but this time
aperitifs, not cider.

"In the state you're in?" she asked.

"Don't you worry about it."

Dagorne, elbow on table, was pursuing his own
idea. His cigarette had gone out and he did not
light it again. The room was emptying out.

"Listen," Le Brix said. "Having thought the
matter out, I think the brother ought to be left
alone. In the first place, as I told you, it's not our
business. Then you've got to think of Jean seeing
his brother arrive one fine day—do you think he'd
have to think twice about that one? No, it can't be
done. It would finish him off."

Dagorne had not thought of that. And yet what
Le Brix was saying was plain common sense. "Does
he know?" he asked.

"I don't know," Le Brix answered, "but I doubt
that he really does. He'll be conscious to the end.
Right now, I wish for only one thing: that he
should die in peace, at home, that he not have to
be taken to the hospital. He's afraid of the hospital,
Dagorne. He hasn't said so, but I know. Come on,
let's get home. It's night already and we should be
on the job early tomorrow."

Marie got up first; her husband's haste to get out
of the inn was a bad sign. Le Brix emptied his glass
and as he pushed it back onto the table, he said:
"And all this because of those sons of bitches. . . ."

IX

As the days went by, Kernevel thought less about
death. In vain he told himself that death was near:
he did not think it had come to that. Except for a
pain that caught him occasionally in the ribs, sweating at night, and some fever, he was not suffering.
But he would have been unable to stand up. In the
morning when Le Brix arrived, he heard him as

though in a dream. Often Le Brix had to go away without having made his bed. There were days when Kernevel did not even answer his friend's questions. The next time Le Brix came he would apologize and say: "I didn't answer you yesterday morning, Fortuné. I was resting."

Le Brix then replied that he had thought so, seeing as how his head had been turned to the wall.

The questions were always the same; and the answers.

"Did you get some sleep?"

"Some."

"Do you need anything?"

"Nothing."

Even his voice was changed. It could hardly be heard, and Le Brix thought of the years gone by, when they had toured France; he thought of the proud Kernevel of those days, his friend, and of the songs he used to sing on the scaffolding. Kernevel's father had taught them to him. He had sung them at full voice, sure of himself and sure to please. He had made all the girls fall in love with him. And now he was moribund. Did he remember his youth? Two or three times Le Brix had tried to recall old memories to him, to talk of old friends with whom they had shared good times. Kernevel had barely answered.

One evening Le Brix had come, as usual, after work. Kernevel was dozing. Gently Le Brix had put a few oranges on the night-table and had left again without making a sound. Kernevel had not stirred. He had heard his friend, but thinking himself on the point of falling asleep, he had not called out to him. But sleep would not come. A few minutes after Le Brix had left, Jean Kernevel turned around on his bed and opened his eyes. The light was on. It was an end-of-October day, silent and softened with rain. He regretted having let Le Brix go. He would have liked someone with him. "What's the matter with me?" he said. "What's come over me?" Peace, a great feeling of tenderness, overtook him. He took a long look around the room and suddenly tears flowed

from his eyes. They were not, as before, tears of
regret. He was not crying for himself, or over his
impending death. They were tears of joy. He did not
know where they came from. He accepted them
gratefully. He looked at the cupboard, the chest of
drawers, and the table and his tears flowed abun-
dantly. He did not dry them. "What's the matter with
me?" he murmured. "What's the matter with me?"
He had heard it said that at the moment of death,
the dying have a moment's respite. "Is this it? Am
I already going to die? Alone?" If this was it, then
death was a great joy. He thought over his life, and
regretted nothing. He felt he had possessed the
friendship of all those whom he had loved, just as
they had possessed his. The rest didn't matter.

He had sat up in bed, the better to see his old
furniture, particularly the cupboard that had been
his mother's, and before that, his grandmother's.
Its brasses had become tarnished since he had taken
to his bed. He reproached himself with not having
asked Marie to give it a touch of polish. He stretched
out his arm and reached out his fingers as though
to touch these things once more. In the drawers of
the chest were his father's pay-book and his service
record. He thought of his father as a comrade. . . .

He fell asleep, and for the first time tasted of
real rest. His sleep was calm, without nightmares,
and when, two or three hours later, he woke up, he
sighed regretfully to think that his joy was over.
His lamp was still lit.

X

Towards the end of the week, they ended their
work in the country. They undertook another job in
town right away. It was in a café, not too far from
Kernevel's; they were re-doing some partitions.
Dagorne brought the news to the sick man. When
he returned, he told Le Brix: "He barely listened to
me. You'd think he was no longer quite with us."

"It's just a matter of days, Dagorne," Le Brix
answered. "And if you want the truth, man, then
I'll tell you that it hurts me quite bad; yes, it hurts

me quite bad, by God!" He threw down the trowel in his hand and broke out sobbing.

Dagorne put a hand on his shoulder.

"Fortuné," he said, "you musn't cry."

"I don't tell it what to do, Dagorne. Just think, I've known him all my life, and if it weren't for their goddam war . . ."

When Le Brix came to Kernevel that noon, he was sitting up in bed, his eyes feverish. As soon as he saw his friend, he raised his hands and cried out: "Come, Fortuné, come on in . . ."

"What's the matter, Jean?"

Kernevel grabbed his hands and squeezed them hard. "You're like a brother to me, Fortuné; tell me what happened."

"Where? What do you mean?"

"Out there, under my window. Less than an hour ago. Some kids were running around my sister and yelling that she was crazy. Why'd they do that? Fortuné, tell me!"

Le Brix tried to escape from Kernevel's grip, but Kernevel resisted and repeated: "Tell me what happened!"

"He's getting delirious," thought Le Brix. "It's the end. I ought to get Houdan."

"Kids, you say?"

"Yes. Why'd they make fun of her?"

"Bah! You've been dreaming, Jean. If you start worrying about things like that, you'll only shorten your days."

Kernevel let go of his hands. He stretched out on his bed.

"Yes," he murmured. "That's what I heard. Perhaps she found out I was sick. She wanted to come and see me. That must be it, Fortuné. Poor Céline: they must have prevented her."

"Wait a moment," said Le Brix, walking to the door. "I'll be right back."

"Where are you going?"

"Wait a moment, I said. I won't be long." Relieved, he left. He went to Houdan and found the

Doctor at lunch. Nevertheless, he received Le Brix.

"He feels worse?"

"Delirious, Doctor."

"I'll be right there. Wait for me."

Together, they returned to Kernevel. While they walked there, Le Brix told the Doctor what had happened, how Kernevel had thought his sister wanted to come and see him.

"She's at the *Incurables,* Doctor. She can't possibly have gotten out."

At first Kernevel did not seem conscious of their presence. Then he opened his eyes and said: "Is that you, Doctor Houdan?"

"Yes, my friend."

"I don't feel well."

"It's a touch of fever. It'll pass. You need care. If you take my advice, you'll let yourself be taken to the hospital. You'll be better off there. . . ."

"Oh, well . . ." Kernevel turned his face to the wall.

"You'll have to get him there right away," Houdan said, lowering his voice.

"All right."

"Go have your lunch. He'll rest a little. He'll feel better in an hour and then you can take him. Get a car, unless you want to have the town ambulance."

"I'll get a car."

"Good. Well then, my friend, I have nothing more to tell you."

"Poor man," murmured Le Brix. "We thank you very much, Doctor, you know, for what you've done. . . . Goodbye."

Dagorne was eating at the Bons Enfants. Le Brix found him there. They lunched together.

"It's the end, Dagorne. He's in a kind of delirium from the fever. Old Houdan said to take him to the hospital. I'm going now."

"Right away?"

"Yes, right away."

"You want me to go with you?"

"No, you get back to work."

Le Brix found a car on the Square. "And if he should still have a fever?" he asked himself as he drove to Kernevel's. "If he should start talking to me about his sister again? Or if he doesn't want to go to the hospital? What do I do?" He regretted not having taken Dagorne with him. But how could Dagorne leave the job? Bah! He wouldn't need any help.

The car stopped at the sidewalk and Le Brix went up the stairs two at a time.

"You've come for me?"

"Yes, old man." He wanted to seem jovial. "You'll be well taken care of there."

Kernevel could not stand up. "Where are my things?"

"I'll help you. Your things are all ready in the cupboard. There they are."

He took out the corduroy trousers, the blue jersey, the jacket, the vest, the boots still spotted with the mud from their last job, and helped Kernevel to dress. When he was ready and Le Brix had put his cap on his head, they went down the stairs.

Kernevel, supported by Le Brix and the driver, sat himself down in the depths of the car; he let himself down on the cushions.

"I'm off to my grave," he said.

Le Brix could not reply. He put his arm around his friend's shoulder.

Kernevel looked through his pockets. "I'm going to give you the key to my trunk. You'll find all my papers in there and a little money. The papers and the money are for my brother Léon."

"Yes, Jean."

"And you'll take my watch."

"Why? I've got one. No, I don't want anything."

"You'll take it in memory of me, Fortuné. That's the way I want it to be."

He lowered his head and Le Brix could not see his face. The car rolled along the paving. Kernevel waited for the noise to stop before going on. "My work things Dagorne can have. We're about the same size and he'll manage. You take my bicycle."

"No, Jean."

"Yes, and my good trowel."

They fell silent. At the hospital door, they shook hands. Two attendants took Kernevel away on a stretcher.

Le Brix returned to work.

"Well?" Dagorne asked.

"He's gone. We'll go see him tomorrow morning."

But when they showed up at the hospital the next morning, they were told that Jean Kernevel had died during the night.

TRANSLATED FROM THE FRENCH
BY KEITH BOTSFORD

A Visit to the Land of

"Did You See Me?

How Was I?"

Possibly one of the less glamorous reasons for Hollywood's being the focal point for the rest of the country (referred to here as the more temperate zone) is that it represents in blowzy minutiae an often accurate forecast of our future attitudes and mannerisms.

The latest in cultural phenomena seem always to have their tryout in the movie colony—a sort of New Haven for the sociologist. One gets the feeling that, given a selective analysis of Hollywood's signs and portents, a national dossier of divorces, domestic muddles, anti-Communist investigations, and unemployment figures could be conveniently projected.

For instance, where, if not Hollywood, did swimming pools, hot rods, rich errant youth, credit living, old-age lobbying, status alcoholism, across-the-board sexuality, psychiatric misinformation, and guilt feelings toward the Nazis get their first big break? Not to mention mediocrity. Whoever heard of mediocrity before movies made it a household definition for a culture?

Not that Hollywood necessarily asked for any of this. Simply by sheer weight of mass attention it has become the vicarious capital of everyone's life. The single unchanging nub of any man's personality is his fantasies. No matter what he's discovered about the world and hard knocks and how it's not all milk and honey, Charlie, his dreams stay pretty much what they were when he was a boy and everything was *beautiful*. And whence came those dreams? Hollywood—the politburo of the American Fantasy. So paranoid with attention and heavy with responsibility it leads us on.

Using the above thesis to fortify us with context, we are ready to look at the present Hollywood scene. It is rife with symptoms. One need only leap into its midst to come away with a plethora of data—all vital, all cogent, all depressing.

Hollywood can be split into four classes. The four classes can then be intersected two by two and interchanged. They are: (1) the migrant; (2) the native; (3) the show biz; (4) the everything-else. Since show biz is the only reason people pay attention to Hollywood, our concern here is with the show-biz migrant and (a more recent breed) the show-biz native.

First let us examine the migrant. Who is it that comes to Hollywood? Earlier, I mentioned the American Fantasy. Now, most of us are quite willing to stay in place and catch the Fantasy as it flies east. But there are those who, like schlock pioneers, must go west to seek it at its source.

Migrants fall into several categories. There is the overstimulated, overassimilated breed—usually found in the mercantile class of show biz. He is very verbal. Yet he has absorbed so much of the character of his surroundings that he's practically invisible. Loud but anonymous. Generally he will be a Reactor. To function normally he will need some other thing to which he can react: an actor, a director, a producer, a film—anything from which he can draw oral sustenance. The Reactor will always carry copies of *Daily Variety* and *The Hollywood Reporter*. He knows what's going on. Since his more intimate conversations are mostly with other reactors, and they *also* know what's going on, the urgency to communicate is limited. The urgency to identify takes precedence. However, since they are all the same person, identification is not much of a problem. A Reactor sounding off to another Reactor will sound like this: "Did you see that flick, sweetheart? Is that a flick? I ask you! Is that beautiful! Beautiful? Don't tell me it's not beautiful! It's beautiful!" His companion will then reply: "You kidding? It's beautiful!"

There is something akin to folk art about this.

Another member of the same group is the Recognizer. Anyone can recognize the stars. The Recognizer, on the other hand, can recognize near-miss stars, screenplay adapters, color consultants, etc. Accosting one of them on the street, he will exude: "Baby, that sound edit job you did on *The Creature from Cape Canaveral*—beautiful! Just beautiful!" In his own way he is a craftsman.

A steadily increasing breed of migrant is the Adjusted Hater. He hates Hollywood and all it stands for and has adjusted to that hate. Yet he loves hating Hollywood and all it stands for and so has adjusted to never leaving. The Adjusted Hater makes a lot of money. Quite often he's a writer and will say, "What do they understand about writing out here?" At other times he's a character actor and will say, "What do they understand about improvisation out here?"

In the past there were few places for the Adjusted Haters to socialize. Late-night rendezvous at fellow haters' homes sufficed for a time but these, because of their transient nature, offered no real atmosphere. More recently Sunset Boulevard has sprouted a number of espresso coffee houses, as pretentiously stark as their New York counterparts, but admirably serving the need for an operational G.H.Q.

Here this internal expatriate may come to sip coffee or beer, listen to folk music, watch mime, and compare life values. His language, likely as not, will be that of the hipster. And this, aside from his basic compromise, will be his strongest similarity to the producers, directors, front-office men, artists' representatives, and agency men whom he despises. The rest of the world may go Hollywood. Hollywood has gone hip.

Jazz musicians, by the very nature of their craft, are outsiders. Hip was a language they created to cut themselves off from the enemy insiders. They should have known better. Though insiders tend to hate nonconformity, they will pirate its safer superficialities every chance they get.

Thus we now have the critic-hipster: "Stanley's direction bugs me. Like I dig his basic attack, but he has a tendency to limit himself to his material. Insecurityville."

Or the executive-hipster: "I swear to you the story line is *wild*. I'm sorry, it's too much. Like I spoke to Marlon and Marlon has eyes. And I spoke to Kirk and Kirk thinks it's a gas. And I spoke to Frank and Frank told me—and this is confidential— Frank told me the plot is *nutty!*"

The hip syndrome is no accident. The quality that hip so perfectly symbolizes is withdrawal from that life which is socially recognizable into that life which is internally unrecognizable. It represents a combustion of alienations. One succeeds in alienating himself from society and then succeeds in alienating himself from himself. Thus, it has charm for the Hollywood personality.

This brings us back to the migrant and his character. What makes a man come to Hollywood in the first place? I contend it is the smog.

Hollywood is a smog-oriented culture. Since air pollution, and now radioactive fallout, have increasingly become a normal condition of living, it would serve us well to note its effect in an environment where casual suffocation has taken on the charming characteristic of a natural resource.

A few words about the esthetics of smog are due here. Smog has lousy esthetics. It is, in and of itself,

a condescension. Not exotic the way fog is, not romantic the way mist is, smog gets along by just
being dull. Carrying no character of its own, it in-
duces dullness in the character of the things it companions. Architecture, to achieve effect, must have
about it a sense of scale. It must have some other
dimension to pose itself against. Sky, for instance.
Hollywood has none. Its architecture, from pink
stucco to Television City modern, all seems to be
dying from some inner and very quiet erosion.

People, too, must have some other dimension to
pose themselves against. Sometimes other people will
do. There are no other people in Hollywood. Perhaps
job-interest will do. There isn't any. And that's why
people come.

It is the lure of mediocrity, the gentle tug of
irresistible inertia. From across the land, they heed
the call of the womb out west where excelling oneself is no problem because no one need bother to try.
Move a genius from N.Y. to L.A. and he becomes a
very bright guy. Old people and talent go there to
retire.

They come to fall, movieland style, into a life of
quasi-fun-and-games. In Beverly Hills the migrants
will get together once a week for golf, once a week
for tennis, once a week for volleyball, and once a
week for poker. There is never any conversation,
except about last week's golf, last week's tennis, last
week's volleyball, or last week's poker. This is not
so much a breakdown of communication as an animal
utilization of it.

Into this world their progeny, the native-born,
sprout. Tall, athletic, and beautiful—vacant-eyed,
slack-jawed, and not too bright. A number of the
young men have been able to refine their level of
interrelating to a few selective grunts and a breath-
taking quantity of fingersnaps. Girls are things to
date when they go out with the fellows to a night
club. If humanity's survival is based on its ability to
change with the times, these kids may well be its
bedrock. There is nothing that, in their trance, they
couldn't adjust to.

It is precisely this trancelike withdrawal which forms the remarkable quality of Hollywood—this nonparticipating social immersion. Outwardly life must be rah-rah, because inwardly it comes up craps.

An actor moves from table to table in a Beverly Hills delicatessen and greets all acquaintances with, "Did you see my Playhouse 90 bit? Did you see me? How was I? Was I beautiful? How was I?"

A radio broadcast begins: "And now fifteen minutes of the latest world news. The Santa Monica Traffic Department instituted a new series of parking regulations yesterday afternoon . . ."

The smogbound city has closed itself off. Its citizens move further into themselves. Their one escape-hatch is their fantasies. And these have been made into movies. So they have fantasies, make movies out of them, and derive their ideas about life from the movie version of the fantasies. Eventually it all gets confused. The fantasies fall under the influence of their screen adaptations. Thus there is the peer fantasy to contend with.

Is it any wonder that amidst all this hugger-mugger the individual must continue his retreat inward? All his interests narrow to himself. Who and what is he? Because he lives in an outdoorsy world he is never alone long enough to find out. So he asks his friends, "Did you see me? How was I? Was I beautiful?" This is called egomania. It is a trade term.

The ego is the only real god in Hollywood. The colony's preoccupation with ridiculous religions is one sign of its basic opposition to a single deity. Every movie star knows he is God. The rest is just outlet. Subconsciously he wants religion, like everything else, to seem nonsensical. Hence the importation of silly cults.

For example, there is Sinatra worship. (He travels with disciples.) The symbol of the over-the-shoulder raincoat obviously suggests the Roman toga and the times of early Christianity. There is Brando worship. The symbol of latent virility suggests the Greeks. The additional symbol of inarticulate sin-

cerity is largely responsible for the Beat Generation
Movement. An outgrowth, or further denomination,
is the Mort Sahlist cult—the worship of Ivy League
irreverence. Sahlists are different from other cultists
because their aim is less to idolize than it is to em-
pathize. The chief and constant worry of any Sahlist
is, "Will Mort sell out?" They will gather in tight
units after his every television appearance and
question whether it should have been done. They
have refocused their doubts about themselves onto
their chosen god. It makes for enormous gratifica-
tion.

What conclusions can we draw from all this? If
Hollywood is indeed an anthropological vanguard,
then the future is one of games and withdrawal.
With the continued growth of mass media, we will
become ever more a nation of Reactors. Action will
be at a decreasing minimum. Inertia will lackadaisi-
cally reign.

The blacklist will be officially rescinded and hosts
of former Government clerical workers, fired for
security reasons, will be able to reclaim their jobs if
they will only apply under assumed names.

The number of Adjusted Haters will multiply.
How many I-hate-the-system-but-what-can-one-guy-
do types there will be is impossible to tell. But there
will be many.

Confusion over the inner self will progress on-
ward. The more our identities muddy, the more
social we'll become—for how else can we know ourselves except by the evaluation of others?

Hip will spread, become diluted and die, only to be
supplanted by a nostalgic revival of hep.

And, of course, our fantasies will grow more commercial. We will, each and every one of us, end up by
getting the girl. Not the prettiest, perhaps, but
certainly the one with the best connections.

faith
in
the
afternoon

As for you, fellow independent thinker of the Western Bloc, if you have anything sensible to say, don't wait. Shout it out loud right this minute. In twenty years, give or take a spring, your grandchildren will be lying in sandboxes all over the world, their ears to the ground, listening for signals from long ago. In fact, kneeling now on the great plains in a snootful of gray dust, what do you hear? Pigs oinking, potatoes peeling, Indians running, winter coming?

Faith's head is under the pillow nearly any weekday midnight, asweat with dreams, and she is seasick with ocean sounds, the squealing wind stuck in its rearing tail by high tide.

That is because her grandfather, scoring the salty sea, skated for miles along the Baltic's icy beaches, with a frozen herring in his pocket. And she, all ears, was born in Coney Island.

Who are her antecedents? Mama and Papa of course. Her environment? A brother and a sister with their own sorrow to lead by the nose out of this

life. All together they would make a goddam quad-
ruped bilingual hermaphrodite. Even so, proving
their excellence, they bear her no rancor and are
always anxious to see her, to see the boys, to take
the poor fatherless boys to a picnic with their boys,
for a walk, to an ocean, glad to say, we saw Mama
in the Children of Judea, she sends love. . . . They
never say snidely, as the siblings of others might,
It wouldn't hurt you to run over, Faith, it's only a
subway ride . . .

Hope and Faith and even Charles—who comes
glowering around once a year to see if Faith's
capacity for survival has not been overwhelmed by
her susceptibility to abuse—begged their parents to
reconsider the decision to put money down and move
into the Children of Judea. "Mother," said Hope,
taking off her eyeglasses, for she did not like even
that little window of glass to come between their
mother and herself. "Now, Mother, how will you
make out with all those *yentas?* Some of them don't
even speak English." "I have spoken altogether too
much English in my life," said Mrs. Darwin. "If I
really liked English that much, I would move to
England." "Why don't you go to Israel?" asked
Charles. "That would at least make sense to people."
"And leave you?" she asked, tears in her eyes at
the thought of them all alone, wrecking their lives
on the shoals of every day, without her tearful gaze
attending.

When Faith thinks of her mother and father in
any year, young or impersonally aged, she notices
that they are squatting on the shore, staring with
light eyes at the white waves. Then Faith feels herself so damply in the swim of things that she con-
siders crawling Channels and Hellesponts and even
taking a master's degree in education in order to
exult at last in a profession and get out of the horse-
shit trades of this lofty land.

Certain facts may become useful. The Darwins
moved to Coney Island for the air. There was not
enough air in Yorkville, where the grandmother had

been planted among German Nazis and Irish bums
by Faith's grandfather, who soon decamped alone in
blue pajamas, for death.

Her grandmother pretended she was German in
just the same way that Faith pretends she is an
American. Faith's mother flew in the fat face of
all that, and once safely among her own kind in
Coney Island, learned real Yiddish, helped Faith's
father, who was not so good at foreign languages,
and as soon as all the verbs and necessary nouns had
been collected under the roof of her mouth, she took
an oath to expostulate in Yiddish and grieve only in
Yiddish and she has kept that oath to this day.

Faith has only visited her parents once since she
began to understand that because of Ricardo she
would have to be unhappy for a while. Faith really
is an American and she was raised up like everyone
else to the true assumption of happiness.

No doubt about it, squinting in any direction she
is absolutely miserable. She is ashamed of this before her parents. "You should get help," says Hope.
"Psychiatry was invented for people like you, Faithful," says Charles. "My little blondie, life is short.
I'll lay out a certain amount of cash," says her
father. "When will you be a person," says her
mother.

Their minds are on matters. Severed Jerusalem;
the Second World War still occupies their arguments; peaceful uses of atomic energy (is it necessary altogether?) ; new little waves of anti-Semitism
lap the quiet beaches of their accomplishment.

They are naturally disgusted with Faith and her
ridiculous position right in the middle of prosperous
times. They are ashamed of her willful unhappiness.

All right! Shame then! Shame on them all!

That Ricardo, Faith's first husband, was a sophisticated man. He was proud and happy because men
liked him. He was really, he said, a man's man. Like
any true man's man, he ran after women too. He was
often seen running, in fact, after certain young

women on West 8th Street or leaping little fences in Bedford Mews to catch up with some dear little pussycat.

He called them pet names which generally referred to certain flaws in their appearance. He called Faith Baldy, although she is not and never will be bald. She is fine-haired and fair, and regards it as part of the lightness of her general construction that when she gathers her hair into an ordinary topknot, the stuff escapes around the contour of her face, making her wisp-haired and easy to blush. He is now living with a shapely girl with white round arms and he calls her Fatty.

When in New York, Faith's first husband lives within floating distance of the Green Coq, a prospering bar where he is well-known and greeted loudly as he enters, shoving his current woman gallantly before. He introduces her around—hey, this is Fatty or Baldy. Once there was Bugsy, dragged up from the gutter where she loved to roll immies with Russell the bartender. Then Ricardo, to save her from becoming an old tea bag (his joke), hoisted her on the pulpy rods of his paperbacked culture high above her class, and she still administers her troubles from there, poor girl, her knees gallivanting in air.

Bugsy lives forever behind the Horney curtain of Faith's mind, a terrible end, for she used to be an ordinarily reprehensible derelict, but by the time Ricardo had helped her through two abortions, and one lousy winter, she became an alcoholic and a whore for money. She soon gave up spreading for the usual rewards, which are an evening's companionship and a weekend of late breakfasts.

Bugsy was before Faith. Ricardo agreed to be Faith's husband for a couple of years anyway, because Faith in happy overindulgence had become pregnant. Almost at once, she suffered a natural miscarriage, but it was too late. They had been securely married by the state for six weeks when that happened, and so, like the gentleman he may very well be, he resigned himself to her love—a

medium-sized beefy-shouldered man, Indian-black
hair, straight and coarse to the fingers, lavender eyes
—Faith is perfectly willing to say it herself, to any
good listener: she loved Ricardo. She began indeed
to love herself, to love the properties which, for a
couple of years anyway, extracted such heart-warm-
ing activity from him.

Well, Faith argues whenever someone says, "Oh,
really, Faithy, what do you mean—love?" She must
have loved Ricardo. She had two boys with him. She
had them to honor him and his way of loving when
sober. He believed and often shouted out loud in
the Green Coq, that Newcastle into which he reeled
every night, blind with coal, that she'd had those kids
to make him a bloody nine-to-fiver.

Nothing, said Faith in those simple days, was
further from her mind. For her public part, she
had made reasoned statements in the playground,
and in the A & P while queued up for the cashier,
that odd jobs were a splendid way of making out if
you had together agreed on a substandard way of
life. For, she explained to the ladies in whom she
had confided her entire life, how can a man know
his children if he is always out working? How true,
that is the trouble with children today, replied the
ladies, wishing to be her friend, they never see their
daddies.

"Mama," Faith said, the last time she visited the
Children of Judea, "Ricardo and I aren't going to be
together so much any more."

"Faithy!" said her mother. "You have a terrible
temper. No, no, listen to me. It happens to many
people in their lives. He'll be back in a couple of
days. After all, the children . . . just say you're
sorry. It isn't even a hill of beans. Nonsense. I
thought he was much improved when he was here a
couple of months ago. Don't give it a thought. Clean
up the house, put in a steak. Tell the children be a
little quiet, send them next door for the television.
He'll be home before you know it. Don't pay attention. Do up your hair something special. Papa would

be more than glad to give you a little cash. We're not poverty-stricken, you know. You only have to tell us you want help. Don't worry. He'll walk in the door tomorrow. When you get home, he'll be turning on the hi-fi."

"Oh, Mama, Mama, he's tone deaf."

"Ai, Faithy, you have to do your life a little better than this."

They sat silently together, their eyes cast down by shame. The doorknob rattled. "My God, Hegel-Shtein," whispered Mrs. Darwin. "Ssh, Faith, don't tell Hegel-Shtein. She thinks everything is her business. Don't even leave a hint."

Mrs. Hegel-Shtein, President of the Grandmothers' Wool Socks Association, rolled in on oiled wheel chair wheels. She brought a lapful of multicolored wool in skeins. She was an old lady. Mrs. Darwin was really not an old lady. Mrs. Hegel-Shtein had organized this Active Association because children today wear cotton socks all winter. The grandmothers who lose heat at their extremities at a terrible clip are naturally more sensitive to these facts than the present avocated generation of mothers.

"Shalom, darling," said Mrs. Darwin to Mrs. Hegel-Shtein. "How's tricks?" she asked bravely.

"Aah," said Mrs. Hegel-Shtein. "Mrs. Essie Shifer resigned on account of her wrists."

"Really? Well, let her come sit with us. Company is healthy."

"Please, please, what's the therapy value if she only sits? Phooey!" said Mrs. Hegel-Shtein. "Excuse me, don't tell me that's Faith. Faith? Imagine that. Hope I know, but this is really Faith. So it turns out you really have a little time to see your mother. . . . What luck for her you won't be busy forever."

"Oh, Celia, I beg you, be quiet," Faith's mortified mother said. "I must beg you. Faith comes when she can. She's a mother. She has two little small boys. She works. Did you forget, Celia, what it was like in those days when they're little babies? Who

comes first? The children . . . the little children,
they come first."

"Sure, sure, first, I know all about first. Didn't
Archie come first? I had a big honor. I got a Christmas card from Florida from Mr. and Mrs. First.
Listen to me, foolish people. I went by them to stay
in the summer place, in the woods, near rivers. Only
it got no ventilation, the whole place smells from
termites and the dog. Please, I beg him, please, Mr.
First, I'm a old woman, be sorry for me, I need extra
air, leave your door open, I beg, I beg. No, not a
word. Bang, every night eleven o'clock, the door gets
shut like a rock. For a ten-minute business they
close themselves up a whole night long.

"I'm better off in a old ladies' home, I told them.
Nobody there is ashamed of a little cross-ventila-
tion."

Mrs. Darwin blushed. Faith said, "Don't be such a
clockwatcher, Mrs. Hegel-Shtein."

Mrs. Hegel-Shtein, who always seemed to know
Faith better than Faith knew Mrs. Hegel-Shtein,
said, "All right, all right. You're here, Faithy, don't
be lazy. Help out. Here. Hold it, this wool on your
hands, your mama will make a ball." Faith didn't
mind. She held the wool out on her arms. Mrs.
Darwin twisted and turned it round and round. Mrs.
Hegel-Shtein directed in a loud voice, wheeling back
and forth and pointing out serious mistakes. "Gittel,
Gittel," she cried, "it should be rounder, you're
making a square. Faithy, be more steadier. Move a
little. You got infantile paralysis?"

"More wool, more wool," said Mrs. Darwin, dropping one completed ball into a shopping bag. They
were busy as bees in a ladies' murmur about life and
lives. They worked. They took vital facts from one
another and looked as dedicated as a kibbutz.

The door to Mr. and Mrs. Darwin's room had
remained open. Old bearded men walked by, thumbs
linked behind their backs, all alike, the left-over
army of the Lord. They had stuffed the morning

papers under their mattresses and because of the
sorrowful current events they hurried up to the
Temple of Judea on the sixth floor, from which
they could more easily communicate with God. Ladies
leaned on sticks stiffly, their articulations jammed
with calcium. They knocked on the open door and
said, "Oi, busy . . ." or "Mrs. Hegel-Shtein, don'
you ever stop?" No one said much to Faith's mother
the Vice-President of the Grandmothers' Wool Socks
Association.

Hope had warned her: "Mother, you are only
sixty-five years old. You look fifty-five." "Youth is
in the heart, Hopey. I feel older than Grandma. It's
the way I'm constituted. Anyway Papa is practically
seventy, he deserves a rest. We have some advantage
that we're young enough to make a good adjustment
By the time we're old and miserable, it'll be like a
home here." "Mother, you'll certainly be an object
of suspicion, an interloper, you'll have enemies
everywhere." Hope had been sent to camp lots of
years as a kid; she knew a thing or two about group
living.

Opposite Faith, her mother swaddled the fat turquoise balls in more and more turquoise wool. Faith
swayed gently back and forth along with her out
stretched wool-wound arms. It hurt her most filial
feelings that in this acute society, Mrs. Hegel-Shtein
should be sought after, admired, indulged. . . .

"Well, Ma, what do you hear from the neighbor
hood?" Faith asked. She thought they could pass
some cheery moments before the hovering shadow of
Ricardo shoved a fat thumb in her eye.

"Ah, nothing much," Mrs. Darwin said.

"Nothing much?" asked Mrs. Hegel-Shtein. "I
heard you correctly said nothing much? You got a
letter today from Slovinsky family, your heart stuck
in your teeth, Gittel, you want to hide this from
little innocent Faith. Little baby Faithy. Ssh. Don'
tell little children? Hah?"

"Celia, I must beg you. I have reasons. I must beg
you, don't mix in. Oh, I must beg you, Celia, not to

push any more, I want to say nothing much on this subject."

"Idiots!" Mrs. Hegel-Shtein whispered low and harsh.

"Did you really hear from the Slovinskys, Mama, really? Oh, you know I'm always interested in Tessie. Oh, you remember what a lot of fun Tess and I used to have where we were kids. I liked her. I never didn't like her." For some reason Faith addressed Mrs. Hegel-Shtein: "She was a very beautiful girl."

"Oh, yeh, beautiful. Young. Beautiful. Very old story. Naturally. Gittel, you stopped winding? Why? The meeting is tonight. Tell Faithy all about Slovinsky, her pal. Faithy got coddled from life already too much."

"Celia, I said shut up!" said Mrs. Darwin. Shut up!"

(Then to all concerned a short dear remembrance arrived. A policeman, thumping after him along the boardwalk, had arrested Mr. Darwin one Saturday afternoon. He had been distributing leaflets for the Sholem Aleichem School and disagreeing reasonably with his second cousin, who had a different opinion about the past and the future. The leaflet cried out in Yiddish: "Parents! A little child's voice calls to you, 'Papa, Mama, what does it mean to be a Jew in the world today?'" Mrs. Darwin watched them from the boardwalk bench, where she sat getting sun with a shopping bag full of leaflets. The policeman shouted furiously at Mr. and Mrs. Darwin and the old cousin, for they were in an illegal place. Then Faith's mother said to him in the Mayflower voice of a disappearing image of life, "Shut up, you Cossack!" "You see," said Mr. Darwin, "to a Jew the word 'shut up' is a terrible expression, a dirty word, like a sin, because in the beginning, if I remember correctly, was the word! It's a great assault. Get it?")

"Gittel, if you don't tell this story now, I roll right out and I don't roll in very soon. Life is life. Everybody today is coddlers."

"Mama, I want to hear anything you know about Tess, anyway. Please tell me," Faith asked. "If you don't tell me, I'll call up Hope. I bet you told her."

"All stubborn people," said Mrs. Darwin. "All right. Tess Slovinsky. You know about the first tragedy, Faith? The first tragedy was she had a child born a monster. A real monster. Nobody saw it. They put it in a home. All right. Then the second child. They went right away ahead immediately and they tried and they had a second child. This one was born full of allergies. It had rashes from orange juice. It choked from milk. Its eyes swoll up from going to the country. All right. Then her husband, Arnold Lever, a very pleasant boy, got a cancer. They chopped off a finger. It got worse. They chopped off a hand. It didn't help. Faithy, that was the end of a lovely boy. That's the letter I got this morning just before you came."

Mrs. Darwin stopped. Then she looked up at Mrs. Hegel-Shtein and Faith. "He was an only son," she said. Mrs. Hegel-Shtein gasped. "You said an only son!" On deep tracks, the tears rolled down her old cheeks. But she had smiled so peculiarly for seventy-seven years that they suddenly swerved wildly toward her ears, and hung like glass from each lobe.

Faith watched her cry and was indifferent. Then she thought a terrible thought. She thought that if Ricardo had lost a leg or so, that would certainly have kept him home. This cheered her a little, but not for long.

"Oh, Mama, Mama, Tessie never guessed what was going to happen to her. We used to play house and she never guessed."

"Who guesses?" screamed Mrs. Hegel-Shtein. "Archie is laying down this minute in Florida. Sun is shining on him. He's guessing?"

Mrs. Hegel-Shtein fluttered Faith's heart. She rattled her ribs. She squashed her sorrow as though it were actually the least toxic of all the world's great poisons.

However, the first one to live with the facts was Mrs. Hegel-Shtein. Eyes dry, she said, "What about

Brauns? The old Braun, an idiot, a regular Irgunist,
is here."

"June Braun?" Faith asked. "My friend June
Braun? From Brighton Beach Avenue? That one?"

"Of course, only, that isn't so bad," Mrs. Darwin
said, getting into the spirit of things. "Junie's husband, an engineer in airplanes. Very serious boy.
Papa doesn't like him to this day. He was in the
movement. They bought a house in Huntington
Harbor with a boat, a garage, a garage for the boat.
She looked stunning. She had three boys. Brilliant.
The husband played golf with the Vice-President, a
goy. The future was golden. She was active in
everything. One morning they woke up. It's midnight. Someone uncovers a little this, a little that. (I
mentioned he was in the movement?) In forty-eight
hours, he's blacklisted. Good night Huntington Harbor. Today the whole bunch live with the Brauns in
four rooms. I'm sorry for the old people."

"That's awful, Mama," Faith said. "The whole
country's in a bad way."

"Still, Faith, times change. This is an unusual
country. You'll travel around the world five times
over, you wouldn't see a country like this often. She's
up, she's down. It's unusual."

"Well, what else, Mama?" Faith asked. June Braun
didn't sorrow her at all. What did June Braun know
about pain? If you go in the dark sea over your head,
you have to expect drowning cheerfully. Faith believed that June Braun and her husband whatever
his name could be had gone too deeply into the air
pocket of America from whence all handouts come,
and she accepted their suffocation in good spirit.

"What else, Mama? I know, what about Anita
Franklin? What about her? God, was she smart in
school! The whole senior class was crazy about her.
Very chesty. Remember her, she got her period
when she was about nine and three-quarters? Or
something like that. You knew her mother very well.
You were always in cahoots about something. You
and Mrs. Franklin. Mama!"

"You sure you really want to hear, Faithy, you

won't be so funny afterward?" She liked telling
these stories now, but she was not anxious to tell
this one. Still she had warned Faith. "All right.
Well, Anita Franklin. Anita Franklin also didn't
guess. You remember she was married way ahead
of you and Ricardo to a handsome boy from Harvard. Oh, Celia, you can imagine what hopes her
mother and her father had for her happiness. Arthur
Mazzano, you know, Sephardic. They lived in Boston
and they knew such smart people. Professors, doctors, the finest people. History-book writers, thinking American people. Oh, Faithy darling. I was invited to the house several times, Christmas, Easter.
I met their babies. Little blondies like you were,
Faith. He got maybe two Ph.D.'s, you know, in
different subjects. If someone wanted to ask a question, on what subject, they asked Arthur. At eight
months their baby walked. I saw it myself. He wrote
articles for Jewish magazines you never heard of,
Celia. Then one day, Anita finds out from the horse's
mouth itself, he is fooling around with Freshmen.
Teen-agers. In no time it's in the papers, everybody
in court, talking talking talking, some say yes, some
no, he was only flirting, you know the way a man
flirts with youngsters. But it turns out one of the
foolish kids is pregnant."

"Spanish people," said Mrs. Hegel-Shtein thoughtfully. "The men don't like their wives so much. They
only get married if it's a good idea."

Faith bowed her head in sorrow for Anita Franklin, whose blood when she was nine and three-quarters burst from her to strike life and hope into the
busy head of all the girls in the fifth and sixth grade.
Anita Franklin, she said to herself, do you think
you'll make it all alone? How do you sleep at night,
Anita Franklin, the sexiest girl in New Utrecht
High? How is it these days, now you are never getting laid any more by clever Arthur Mazzano, the
brilliant Sephardic Scholar and Lecturer? Now it is
time that leans across you and not handsome, fair
Arthur's mouth on yours, or his intelligent boy
scouty conflagrating fingers.

At this very moment, the thumb of Ricardo's hovering shadow jabbed her in her left eye, revealing for all the world the shallowness of her water table. Rice could have been planted at that instant on the terraces of her flesh and sprouted in strength and beauty in the floods that overwhelmed her from that moment on through all the afternoon. For herself and Anita Franklin, Faith bowed her head and wept. She suffered her own Indonesia.

"Going already, Faith?" her father asked. He had poked his darling birdy head with poppy pale eyes into the sunspotted room. He is not especially good-looking. He is ugly. Faith has often thanked the Germ God and the Gene Goddess and the Great Lords of All Nucleic Acid that none of them look like him, not even Charles, to whom it would not matter, for Charles has the height for any kind of face. They all look a little bit Teutonish, like their grandmother, who thinks she's German, just kind of light and even-featured with Charles inclining to considerable jaw. People expect decision from Charles because of that jaw, and he has learned to give it to them—the wit of diagnosis, then inescapable treatment, followed by immediate health. In fact, his important colleagues often refer their wives' lower abdominal distress to Charles. Before he is dead he will be famous. Mr. Darwin hopes he will be famous soon, for in that family people do not live long.

Well, this popeyed, pale-beaked father of Faith's peered through the room into the glassy attack of the afternoon sun, couldn't focus on tears, or bitten lips for that matter, but saw Faith rise to look for her jacket in the closet.

"If you really have to go, I'll walk you, Faithy. Sweetheart, I haven't seen you in a long time," he said. He withdrew to wait in the hallway, well out of the circle of Mrs. Hegel-Shtein's grappling magnetism.

Faith kissed her mother, who whispered into her damp ear, "Be something, don't be a dishrag. You have two babies to raise." She kissed Mrs. Hegel-

Shtein, because they had been brought up that way, not to hurt anyone's feelings, particularly if they loathed them, and they were much older.

Faith and her father walked through the light-green halls in silence to the life-giving lobby, where rosy, well-dressed families continued to arrive in order to sit for twenty minutes alongside their used-up elders. Some terrible political arguments about Jews in Russia now were taking place near the information desk. Faith paid no attention but moved toward the door, breathing deeply. She tried to keep her father behind her until she could meet the commitments of her face. "Don't rush, sweetheart," he said. "Don't rush, I'm not like these old cockers here, but I am no chicken definitely."

Gallantly he took her arm. "What's the good word?" he asked. "Well, no news isn't bad news, I hope?"

"So long, Chuck!" he called as they passed the iron gate over which in stunning steel cursive, a welder had inscribed "The Children of Judea." "Chuckle, Chuckle," said her father, grasping her elbow more firmly, "what a name for a grown-up man!"

She turned to give him a big smile. He deserved an enormous smile, but she had only a big one available.

"Listen, Faithl, I wrote a poem, I want you to hear. Listen. I wrote it in Yiddish, I'll translate it in my head:

> Childhood passes
> Youth passes
> Also the prime of life passes.
> Old age passes.
> Why do you believe, my daughters,
> That old age is different?

"What do you say, Faithy? You know a whole bunch of artists and writers."

"What do I say? Papa." She stopped stock-still. "You're marvelous. That's like a Japanese Psalm of David."

"You think it's good?"

"I love it, Pa. It's marvelous."

"Well . . . you know, I might give up all this political stuff, if you really like it. I'm at a loss these days. It's a transition. Don't laugh at me, Faithy. You'll have to survive just such events some day yourself. Learn from life. Mine. I was going to organize the help. You know, the guards, the elevator boys—colored fellows, mostly. You notice, they're coming up in the world. Regardless of hopes, I never expected it in my lifetime. The war, I suppose, did it. Faith, what do you think? The war made Jews Americans and Negroes Jews. Ha, ha. What do you think of that for an article? 'The Negro: Outside in at Last.' "

"Someone wrote something like that."

"Is that a fact? It's in the air. I tell you, I'm full of ideas. I don't have a soul to talk to. I'm used to your mother, only a funny thing happened to her, Faithy. We were so close. We're still friendly, don't take me the wrong way, but I mean a funny thing, she likes to be with the women lately. Loves to be with that insane, persecution, delusions of grandeur, paranoical Mrs. Hegel-Shtein. I can't stand her. She isn't a woman men can stand. Still, she got married. Your mother says, be polite Gersh; I am polite. I always loved the ladies to a flaw, Faithy, but Mrs. Hegel-Shtein knocks at our room at nine A.M. and I'm an orphan till lunch. She has magic powers. Also she oils up her wheel chair all afternoon so she can sneak around. Did you ever hear of a wheel chair you couldn't hear coming? My child, believe me, what your mother sees in her is a shady mystery. How could I put it? That woman has a whole bag of spitballs for the world. And also a bitter crippled life."

They had come to the subway entrance. "Well, Pa, I guess I have to go now. I left the kids with a friend."

He shut his mouth. Then he laughed. "Aaah, a talky old man. . . ."

"Oh, no, Pa, not at all. No. I loved talking to you, but I left the kids with a friend, Pa."

"I know how it is when they're little, you're tied

down, Faith. Oh, we couldn't go anywhere for years.
I went only to meetings, that's all. I didn't like to
go to a movie without your mother and enjoy myself. They didn't have babysitters in those days. A
wonderful invention, babysitters. With this invention
two people could be lovers forever."

"Oh!" he gasped, "my darling girl, excuse
me . . ." Faith was surprised at his exclamation
because the tears had come to her eyes before she
felt their pain.

"Ah, I see now how the land lies. I see you have
trouble. You picked yourself out a hard world to
raise a family."

"I have to go, Pa."

"Sure."

She kissed him and started down the stairs.

"Faith," he called, "can you come soon?"

"Oh, Pa," she said, four steps below him, looking
up, "I can't come until I'm a little happy."

"Happy!" He leaned over the rail and tried to
hold her eyes. But that is hard to do, for eyes are
born dodgers and know a whole circumference of
ways out of a bad spot. "Don't be selfish, Faithy,
bring the boys, come."

"They're so noisy, Pa."

"Bring the boys, sweetheart. I love their little
goyish faces."

"O.K., O.K.," she said, wanting only to go quickly.
"I will, Pa, I will."

Mr. Darwin reached for her fingers through the
rail. He held them tightly and touched them to her
wet cheeks. Then he said, "Aaah . . ." an explosion
of nausea, absolute digestive disgust. And before she
could turn away from the old age of his insulted face
and run home down the subway stairs, he had
dropped her sweating hand out of his own and
turned away from her.

THE WORLD AS A VISION
OF THE UNITY IN FLESH

One Paris in the morning
Altogether without warning
All together all the lovers
Touching under clumsy covers
Nose to nose and feet to feet
Started dreaming in their heat

All the lovers started dreaming
And they dreamed their dreams of those
Who lay dreaming under covers
Close beside their newer lovers
Who were dreaming dreams of others
Feet to feet and nose to nose

A POET IS DWELLING IN HARLEM

High within his tower of horn
He only hears the distant moan
Of rhymesters buried by the Thames.
Amidst bad dreams he knows the wrens
In chatters of typewriter, thinks of Bach's
Long-playing unbreakable metrical shocks
And fails to note this ebony voice
Come bouncing from the lowly street
"Who, me? Jus' happy as a clam!
Don't twiss my ear in a pretzel, damn,
You talks as long as niney-dollas
In pennies, man!"

George P. Elliott

CRITIC AND COMMON READER

I

One of the sadnesses of the age is that the idea of the Common Reader has fallen away so far. The word "common" itself has dwindled. Henry Wallace's common man has little to do with Dr. Johnson's common reader: "I rejoice to concur with the common reader; for, by the common sense of readers uncorrupted with literary prejudices, after all the refinements of subtilty and the dogmatism of learning, must be finally decided all claim to poetical honors." Perhaps it is true that modern times have so fragmented and troubled us that nearly all actual readers have been made into specialists of some kind, or else use literature as a drug for killing time and dulling anxiety. Even so, the ideal of writing for the mature, experienced, cultivated Common Reader ought not to be allowed to perish—that Common Reader whom Virginia Woolf considered herself to be when she wrote her superb essays. Editors of books and magazines too often think of markets:

fashion magazines, sex magazines, little magazines; historical book club, science book club, detective story book club; the Catholic novel, the Jewish novel, the novel of Southern decadence, the avant-garde novel. To be sure, the world being so incalculable a place as it is, things often won't stay in their cubby-holes; it was pleasing to see how *Lolita*'s popular success confounded everybody hopelessly. All the same, the way of thinking of readers as specialists has affected even writers, until they think of them-selves as "aiming at a market." This wouldn't matter much if it didn't begin to have some effect on good writers, for some of whom popularity has become a proof of mediocrity. For some literary intellectuals nowadays the only market worth aiming at is the company of the best, into which, so they are per-suaded, ordinary folk can never be admitted. A few even seem to think that commoners are a sort of reverse Midas: their touch turns gold back into something base. *Finnegans Wake* is their book of books, impermeable and unalloyed; not even Auden, Barzun, and Trilling had read it through, so they confessed, when they recommended it in January 1956 to the members of that highbrow book club, The Readers' Subscription.

For literature has its fire-belching dragons guard-ing hoards of what they say is golden treasure—Yvor Winters, for example, or Northrup Frye, or Robert Graves. Word of them gets around, and travelers show you little pieces of pure gold which they claim to have gotten from the hoard of one of the dragons. So maybe some day you make the journey to his marvelous cave, wait till he is off guard, and rush in. And indeed there are pots of stuff that shines like gold; you pocket a few pieces and steal away; and if you were very lucky, maybe they are gold as fine as there is in the world. But probably not; probably what you get for your trouble is copper or brass or gold-plated lead. (Not that the dragon him-self is a phony; he really believes that his hoard is pure bullion, that it was gold when *he* had it, that it was your touch that debased it.)

But the common reader lives in a more sociable country. He is like a citizen of a free and upright republic, in which most of the power is wielded by the patricians, who correspond to the writers and critics. Yet these very patricians are no more than free citizens themselves in the eyes of the law, and they must not forget, even during an age of Caesars, that the power they exercise comes from and reverts to the people. For when the state becomes too corrupt any longer to require responsibility of its citizens, some require it of themselves. They are worth writing for, always.

But how can a critic be a Common Reader? He reads all the time, he practically reads as a profession, and when he's not reading he writes about what he's read, and when he's not reading and writing, he talks about books, either as a teacher or else with his friends. He knows a great deal, about literary history, the lives of writers, the arts of writing. What's common about him? Very little, most of the time. There aren't many good critics, not nearly so many good critics as good poets—which is as it should be. All the same, since we now live in an age when critics flourish as never before, I think it worthwhile to look at the vocation of critic with some attention.

To define a critic negatively, by a critic I do not mean an esthetician, for he is interested in theories of beauty and in general principles, being a philosopher. Nor a literary historian, for he, being a historian, is interested in cause and effect among works of literature and between them and social forces. Nor an anthologist, for he is usually little more than an encyclopedist and archivist. One could, however, make a sort of case for some anthologies as being fine works of criticism; there are not many contemporary books of criticism which seem to me to be superior in their kind to Walter de la Mare's wonderful anthologies, *Come Hither, Behold This Dreamer,* and *Love.* Nor a scholar, though by a curiosity of history there exists a topsy-turvy world where scholars have more status and power than critics, and both have a hundred times more than writers—in the universities, where most literary people earn their living. In the looking-glass world of academic importance, knowing about literature is much more marketable than having your own opinions about it, and both fetch a higher price than writing it. But true scholars, who are usually humble about their calling, see themselves as servants to literature; the recovery, editing, and publication of the Boswell papers is a pure example of scholarship doing what it best can, bringing a text to readers, and the scholars involved, who did the work because they enjoyed doing it, merit the gratitude they have been accorded. But there are two main categories of literateurs who, to my thinking, should not be confused with critics—book reviewers and exegetes.

A book reviewer, because he hasn't time to allow his experience of the book he has just read to mellow and grow (or to wither and rot), is not a full critic, for when a critic talks responsibly about a book, one of his important considerations is how thoroughly the book has become an enduring part of his mind. My case about reviewing versus criticism has been made for me by as eminent a reviewer as the country has ever produced. Edmund Wilson, in an interview last year, to the question "What do you think of the standards of literary criticism today?" gave the following answer:

> I don't think about those things AT ALL! Literary criticism is a department of literature for me, and when I read literary critics I read them as literature; the others I can't read at all. I never think of myself, for instance, as a literary critic; I think of myself simply as a writer and a journalist.●

An exegete is not a critic either, for his concern is to explain and reveal (originally he dealt with holy writ). He prefers a work of literature in which meanings are hidden, or else he claims there is no other kind. He looks at the structure of a short story not because it is beautiful but because he believes

● *New Republic*, March 30, 1959.

some of the meaning is to be found in the structure
itself. He looks for ambiguities, irony, allegory,
symbolic values. Take the tiger in Blake's poem. I
have heard it identified as sin, evil, the destructive
power of the universe, Satan, and Christ. Once I
demurred—to the man who called the tiger Christ—
and suggested that the tiger is a tiger. Oh, the embarrassment with which he told me, "Yes, yes, on
that level to be sure." Imagine a great and grave
poet troubling to write about a mere tiger! This
incomprehension on the exegete's part comes, I
think, from his own disinclination to enjoy a poem
for *its* sake; in his hierarchy, understanding is
superior to enjoyment. He, looking at a poem, sees
more significance than poetry; he may see the poem
as a sort of hatrack for meanings to hang on. "The
meaning is the beauty"—an energetic statement like
"beauty is truth, truth beauty," emitting more heat
than light. So how can he believe that a poet looking
at a tiger sees, overwhelmingly, a tiger? Did you
ever *look* at a tiger? Did you ever try to imagine
what a tiger *is?* The grandfather of the contemporary school of secular exegesis (commonly known
as the New Criticism) is I. A. Richards, who wrote
one of its books of secular theology, *The Meaning of
Meaning;* and the most influential handbook in the
technique of modern exegesis is entitled *Understanding Poetry*—not experiencing or enjoying it, but
understanding it.

At this point I am afraid I am splitting imaginary
hairs. Of course Cleanth Brooks has written some
very fine essays in criticism, just as Richards has
written not only some splendid criticism but also a
few good poems. And T. S. Eliot, who is a critic if
ever there was one, reviewed books by the dozen
and furthermore some of his more celebrated essays
were written as book reviews. And as for scholars,
Dr. Johnson, who invented the Common Reader in
the first place, was a critic *and* a scholar.

Essentially a critical essay, whatever else it may
contain, is a creative form of writing; it does not
aim to impart information to a reader, so much as

to generate attitudes and emotions in him. Its subject is less an idea than an experience of literature, whether of a single story, or the total work of a poet, or a group of novels, or dramatic tragedy as a type. An essay which aims to communicate something of a valuable experience, or to re-create in the reader an experience analogous to it, is obviously a work of literature itself, though the experience used may be one of literature. It is quite possible for more to happen to a man when he reads *Don Quixote* than in a month of ordinary living, and if he then tells you about what happened to him, he is essaying criticism. To be sure, a good critic will be more learned than an ordinary reader; he will be possessed of a highly developed literary style; his judgment will be sound, though whenever he feels a conflict between that soundness and a fidelity to his own quirky experience, his experience wins; his discriminations will be fine; and he will be specially capable of joy in words, and in the sorts of experience which words can get at. All the same, because he both aims at the audience a poet aims at and at the same time *is* that audience, the critic may be any sort of specialist he wants to be, from esthetician to literary journalist to expert on place names in the *Morte d'Arthur;* but he must also, to avoid temptation, consider himself that imaginary creature the Common Reader.

II

The moment a critic despairs of his true calling, all sorts of temptations invite him to pervert his talents. Much the most interesting such perversions are those of esotericism; the fires and roars of the dragons are pretty impressive, and there is some gold in their hoards. But the blatant perversions from the critic's true way are those of vulgarity, of acting stupider than he is.

Suppose that a man who has the capacity for true criticism drifts instead into vulgar criticism. Is it a case simply of selling out? It may be, in which event it is just another form of hypocrisy. But most of the time when a critic turns vulgar, he does something much subtler and more dangerous than selling books hypocritically: he confuses excellence with recognition. Maybe he does it because he wants money and fame, maybe he does it out of sincere conviction, maybe he doesn't even know he's doing it; but his motives are of very little importance compared to the confusion he causes.

One form of this is to use popularity for more than it's worth in gauging literary excellence. Only a sales-manager up to his gills in cocktails is imbecilic enough to think of popularity as *it*, and only a desert saint who's sure of his supply of manna can hold that there's never a connection between excellence and popularity. But in between, you're apt to come on statements like the one made by John O'Hara when the 1959 National Book Award for fiction was given to Bernard Malamud:

> I believe it should be the duty of the National Book Award jury to reward the all-out professional author and not dig around like a truffle hound to rescue some unknown writer from obscurity. He's most likely not a readable writer. In this country the good writer does get read. I don't believe that there are any better writers than Hemingway, Steinbeck, Faulkner, Cozzens, and I— pining away down in Brown County, Indiana, or in an espresso joint on West Third Street in Greenwich Village.•

This general view has been put somewhat less petulantly. George Orwell, who shared with most people a lack of enthusiasm for poetry, makes the main character of *Keep the Aspidistra Flying* choose between writing poetry and affirming the aspidistra, which for him means creating a family and writing advertising copy. In the next to last chapter, he takes the manuscript of his long poem out of his pocket, "a great wad of paper, soiled and tattered," "the sole fruit of his exile, a two years' foetus which would never be born. Well he had finished with all that. Poetry! *Poetry,* indeed! In 1935." And he stuffs it down a sewer drain. There's a legitimate and formidable question here: If in fact ordinary people don't read it, how can you possibly say it was

• *New York World-Telegram and Sun,* March 6, 1959.

written for the Common Reader? There's an allied
question, which is even trickier: How can you know
when a book is very good? Later on I shall deal with
them both at once.

A more important confusion which a critic can fall
into concerns authority and excellence. Well, this is
a dilemma everyone's hung up on, more or less, at
one time or another. You can't go through school
without knowing the "received" opinion toward
Shakespeare; thousands upon thousands of children
have been kept from liking Shakespeare's plays by
reason of heavy-handed authority; but, before a
group of even halfway literate people, it takes a
revolutionary to maintain that he doesn't like Shakespeare, and a very Trotsky to maintain that Shakespeare is no good. It is simply absurd to reject whole-
sale the recommendations of authorities. After all, it
is because of them that most of us know the good
writers are there at all. Eliot spake: and behold,
there was Donne. Authority tells you to read *War
and Peace,* so read it; you can't read all the books,
and it's probably good; you'll probably like it or learn
to like it. Mickey Spillane was for a few years the
most popular writer in the United States; but authority tells you his thrillers are garbage; very well,
if you read one of them as a way of killing time and
don't pretend you're doing something worth doing,
little harm will befall you, though no good. But if it
is absurd to reject authorities outright, it is repulsive
to kowtow to them. Suppose the *Aeneid,* which they
tell you to read, preferably in Latin, bores you in
English. You don't have to be obnoxious about not
liking it, but at least don't pretend to others that
you do and certainly don't tell yourself that you do.
It is far better to enjoy *King Solomon's Mines* by
H. Rider Haggard than to like the *Aeneid* just because you think you ought to.

There are also a couple of vulgar traps for those
who wield the authority. For one thing, the man of
authority may himself become popular; so much the
better; but then he may aquire a taste for popularity, and especially he may acquire a taste for being

rubbed up against by popularity's half-naked little handmaiden, flattery. "How true, how wise, how beautifully put. What do you think of James's late novels?" Well, maybe this man of distinction has never thought about James's late novels, or even read them, for that matter; but he's pretty sure to know what the two main going opinions on them are. For some more of those melting looks of adorers he's willing to spout some likely opinion or other; maybe he'll feel in the mood to complain that the late James loses himself in the subtleties of his own style whereas the earlier James . . . Maybe he'll take the other line. Either of them can, expertly taken, produce good results. I even saw both at once, in the hands of two critics who were agreeing to disagree, generate in the sitters-by blending purrs of adulation for both experts simultaneously.

A more important vulgar trap for those with authority consists in their acquiescing to become a part of that whole system of imposition for which "Madison Avenue" is a nickname. For whatever complex of reasons, most of them dreadful, readers seem to have become increasingly passive in choosing their books. People generally seem to be allowing themselves to be told what to do, what to think, how to enjoy themselves. An external symptom of this tendency in book-buying (and therefore, presumably, in book-reading) is the decline of bookstores in the country and the rise of book clubs. When people bought their books in a well-stocked store, they more often than not chose for themselves and much more often chose non-best-sellers. Now that people buy most of their books through book clubs, they restrict their choice to one of a few guaranteed selections and they are apt to prefer a best-seller. Well, since book clubs are what people seem to want—or can be persuaded to want—and since there are well-oiled machineries for satisfying this want, obviously some authorities are needed to choose the master-piece of the month and to assure and reassure the customers of its masterpieceliness. Let us imagine the history of such a judge.

Suppose him to be a professor at Columbia. Why Columbia? For excellent reasons. Columbia has a lot of prestige, not as much as Harvard, to be sure, but enough. And it is in New York. This means that our professor, who is personable, goes to some of the more important literary parties, where business and liquor are plentifully combined, and makes contacts. It also means that some of his students are likely to become reviewers, editors, publishers—men of power, the men who choose the book club judges. Further, suppose our professor to be a sound scholar, to which much popular prestige attaches, to have his own taste and to have the courage to persuade you of its soundness. In other words, here is a man who could be, and sometimes is, a critic and who deserves respect and commands it. But the masterpiece a month must be chosen, and he is asked to help choose it. Now the office pays well, it entails a certain fame, and it certainly offers power in a form that appeals to professors. The rationalization runs along lines something like these: There are so many books being published that ordinary people can't be expected to choose wisely; you are a man with the courage of his own taste and with the qualifications to choose well; you are beautifully situated to know what is going on in the literary world, of publishing and criticism as well as of writing; book clubs serve a real social purpose by saving people money and by giving writers a large audience; there is no question of bribery, of pay-offs by publishers; your choice will be made on the basis of your own judgment and only of that. Why not? And sometimes it works quite well. Our professor gets one of Thomas Mann's best novels to a lot of people who very well might not otherwise have read it; he feels good. But there are other masterpiece-of-the-month clubs with panels of honorable judges, and it turns out that the current supply of masterpieces is limited, especially of masterpieces of the kind which several score thousand readers nowadays are apt to enjoy. Still and all . . . Everything possible is done to make him believe: *If you choose it, it must be pretty good.* And he can coast along in this slick confusion for an indefinite time. The money-men who run the show, the experts in the techniques of imposition, the masses who are grateful to him for telling them what is worth reading, the honey-gold tongues of flattery, all help him not to think too carefully about why he chose, or allowed to be chosen, such books as *The Enemy Camp,* which may on literary grounds be worth reading but which is not a masterpiece, or *Aku-Aku,* which may be worth reading, or *Only in America.* The professor's regard for Horace and Catullus and Juvenal, Chaucer and Malory and Spenser, remains undiminished; his opinions about them are entirely unconfused; perhaps he is still capable of reading them as fully as he once did, perhaps not. What shall we call our power professor? A pretty good name for him would be Jacques Van Doren Highet. A name like that could sell 50,000 copies of the Graustark national epic in the original Fenugreek.

III

The errors of esotericism, as I conceive the matter, are closely connected with, and sometimes derive from, a dangerous ailment among literary folk. It is not a new disease, and it's seldom fatal; yet it is important enough to be worth mentioning. It holds that we should settle for nothing less than master-pieces—*we* being readers, critics, writers, teachers, anyone concerned with literature. You hear this view stated or implied in a thousand forms. It was Cyril Connolly who made the case most obnoxiously. "The more books we read . . ." (this is a different *we;* count me out)

> The more books we read, the sooner we perceive that the true function of a writer is to produce a masterpiece and that no other task is of any consequence. . . . Writers engrossed in any literary activity which is not their attempt at a masterpiece are their own dupes and, unless these self-flatterers are content to write off such activities as their contribution to the war effort, they might as well be peeling potatoes.

These two sentences occur on the first page of *The Unquiet Grave.* Since the book itself is no masterpiece—I hope for Mr. Connolly's sake he was not attempting one—it provides as neat an instance as you could ask for of "Do as I say, not as I do."

Last year I heard an eminent poet in his forty-first year assert that, between the time when Pound and Eliot burst on the scene until just recently when there appeared an American and an Englishman both around thirty, there had been no new poet in English. The ailment has a melancholy form which afflicts writers sometimes, comparing everything you write to the best that has been thought and said; in very severe cases, like that of Matthew Arnold the poet, who "threw his gift in prison till it died," the writer quits writing altogether.

And this is what I have against the masterpiece-or-nothing theory: it is against life. It is literary Calvinism with a vengeance: a book is either one of the elect, and there aren't many of those, or one of the damned. But a man who is full of life is not so keen on this butchery of experience. Sometimes he is up to reading *Paradise Lost,* to be sure, but most of the time he is not; he finds Dostoevsky a marvelous but awfully rich diet; when he sees *A Doll's House,* he is stirred deeply, but sometimes he doesn't feel like stirring. He sees no reason to cast the novels of Kingsley Amis, Ramón Sender, or Jean Giono into outer darkness; he has moods in which he finds the poems of Stephen Spender or William Carlos Williams just about great enough for him; he is unabashed in his enjoyment of both *Pygmalion* and *My Fair Lady;* and the reason he gave for liking Charlie Chaplin's movies was that they were fun.

There are sound critical reasons to distrust the masterpiece approach to literature. One of them is that it violates a sense of history, of the context into which a book is embedded and out of which it has emerged. Scholarship has done us—all of us— a fine service by insisting upon our exercising historical imagination to the limit of our knowledge and power; I am sure that such a writer as Chaucer has been recovered for the Common Reader in good part because of the development of this faculty, which was long slighted. But if exercising historical imagination permits one to enjoy all sorts of works which otherwise would be lost, how much truer it is that books contemporary with the reader may speak to him with a living voice in tones he recognizes. And here, the *Meisterstück-über-alles* attitude is especially pernicious. I resent, more than I will say, being told that until three or four years ago there hadn't appeared a new poet in English since the 1910's. I do not benefit from such an attempt to demolish a whole delightful shire of my experience, a shire which includes poetry by Auden, Eberhart, Schwartz, Miles, Dylan Thomas, and a dozen more. Maybe there's not a great poet among them; I don't really care; I don't like to read in order to judge and pigeonhole. But they have told me in poetry about the world I live in and myself, they have given me pleasure, they have become part of me. Just as I would hate to have for neighbor a man who will love only saints, so I wish all the nothing-less-than-masterpiece monsters would get back up into the hills where they belong and guard caves.

Still, one should be glad the literary cultists are there, for they keep things toned up. Their roarings can be heard for miles, and they can make sitting in a chair with a book in your hand a risky adventure. But if there's anything they have no use for, it's Common Readers. The impulse to make a cult of Shakespeare must be terribly frustrated by his egregious popularity, in all ages, in many languages, among all classes of mankind. I suppose this impulse, hard put to find something inaccessible about Shakespeare, generated the absurdities about who *really* wrote the plays. At any rate, the squabbles over authorship are not engaged in just by crackpots, unless you think Freud was cracked. He believed that Shakespeare's plays were written by the Earl of Oxford. (He was persuaded to this view by a man named Looney.)

Cultism is a matter of attitude, of being in on a secret which you, you dolt, aren't in on, and cultists commonly find treasure among the obscure and/or difficult. Yvor Winters is a master at this sort of thing; according to him, one of the most considerable nineteenth-century American poets is Jones Very; one of the two or three supreme poets in English is Fulke Greville; and as for the greatest poem there is, he names *Ebauche d'un serpent* by Paul Valéry. But he doesn't stop with naming this poem; he goes on to exalt the type to which it belongs, the short poem.

> The epic and the poetic drama, for example, have long been dead, and I did not kill them. . . . The novel, for the most part an abortive form from its beginnings, is dying rapidly. . . . The writers of the short poem have done very well, if one regards them over a long period, and they are definitely alive today; but I am convinced that greater achievements are possible in the short poem and that we would have a better chance of such achievements if we could bring ourselves to understand the nature of the form and the fact that this form is the greatest form, of all forms the one most suited to communication among those who are wholly civilized and adult.●

Well, since Mr. Winters assumes (perhaps somewhere he states it) that literature is the highest form of human activity, that makes Valéry's poem the greatest achievement of the human mind, anytime, anywhere.

Or there are paper dragons like Tiffany Thayer, who kept his hoard in a thimble; he led the Fortean Society, which is dedicated to the books of Charles Fort; Fort believed, among other things, that the firmament is composed of a sort of perforated gelatin and that spooks abound. Or there are very ambitious dragons like Robert Graves; he maintains that *all* poetry is hidden from the many, is essentially occult; if it isn't occult, it isn't poetry: Q.E.D. Or there are Frye-types who think that some works of literature, or even literature itself, provides the key whereby the secret meaning of life may be unlocked.

The most bellowish dragon I know of nowadays is Hugh Kenner. His roars are so hard on the ears that they prevent one from attending to what he's roaring about; I was kept off Pound and Wyndham Lewis

● *Function of Criticism* (Alan Swallow, 1957), p. 74.

very effectively by Kenner's lashings and gnashings,
and I'm glad I got to Eliot, Joyce, and Yeats before
Kenner got to me. This is from a book review of his:

> To be the best poet practising in England is, these days,
> to share a meaningless eminence with the wittiest
> statistician in Terre Haute or the handsomest peacock
> ever hatched in Idaho. It is therefore virtually useless to
> locate Mr. Tomlinson with reference to his contempo-
> raries.●

I know that Kenner's hoard contains some 24-carat
treasure, and I do hope it's gold he's got in his
Tomlinson pot. But I'm afraid, after wincing through
this review, it'll be some time before I even glance
at the book he thought he was recommending. (You
remember that other dragon who said there'd only
been one British poet in the past forty years? Well,
Tomlinson wasn't that poet; that was Philip Larkin.
And this dragon is himself a poet who has recently
been called, by a lesser dragon, the only English-
writing poet of the twentieth century deserving to be
ranked with Yeats. Someone should make a daisy-
chain of dragons.) My favorite quotation from
Kenner comes in the form of a simple declarative
sentence which means exactly what it says. The Vortex he speaks of was a group of friends, consisting
of Pound, Lewis, Eliot, Ford Madox Ford, and
Gaudier-Brzeska (whoever he was), "with Joyce a
saluted ally," and with Yeats standing in the wings
where he was called on by Pound every Monday evening. The Vortex lasted from 1914 to 1916. I am
quoting out of context, but nothing in what he says
before or after modifies the dragonism of this statement:

> That World War I dissipated the Vortex may yet prove
> to have been its most far-reaching effect.●●

IV

By this time, if you, dear reader, have not developed a considerable opposition to what I've been saying, you're a lot more placid than I am. For example,

● *Poetry*, February 1959.
●● *Gnomon* (McDowell, Obolensky, 1958), p. 147.

I share the general critical opinion that Blake and Yeats are very great poets. Yet they are esoterics if ever men were. I have heard that on theosophical bookshelves Yeats's preposterous book *A Vision* stands not far from Mme Blavatsky's *Isis Unveiled*. Preposterous, yes, but he took *A Vision* seriously and it's conceivable that one would enjoy more of his poems, and enjoy them more thoroughly, for reading it. Is it not true that there are coigns and chasms of unknowledge everywhere man looks—in the physical world, in all that lives, within his own mind, in literature? Any Common Reader who ever opened his eyes at night knows this, and furthermore he puts more trust in a Blake than in writers who spread the answers out in smooth array for him to savor. Still, the occult as such does not charm him, and he balks when the cultists push at him too hard.

I am not easy in my position, for I know the truth is hidden; I know that to expose it in clear daylight is to dry it up and change its hue. I know that most of us lead our lives badly, do not want to change, do not want even to be reminded that we should change; we need prophets like Blake. I know that such men as Robert Graves and Yvor Winters have splendid and passionate minds and have written not only some of the best literary criticism I have read but also genuine poetry. Furthermore, I think poetry itself is mysterious both because poetry uses familiar words in an esoteric way and because words themselves are mysterious and full of risk. The Word . . .

Earlier, I posed two questions, which I hope now to answer. The first is: If ordinary people don't in fact read or like a book, how can you say it was written for the Common Reader? You can't. But you can say you are convinced from reading that book that, when time and Authority offer it to the Common Reader, he will like it. Blake illustrates this contention; he thought he was writing his poetry for everyone; it has turned out that he was right, for at least part of it, the short poems rather than the Prophecies. Pindar, however, presents the problem in a different way. He has the reputation of a

great poet, yet twenty-five centuries have not sufficed
to give him popularity. He was an aristocrat writing
for aristocrats, and he has been read almost exclu-
sively by the literary elite; yet they, a good many of
whom like to concur with the Common Reader, insist
with persuasive vigor that Pindar is one of the supreme lyric poets. What to do? The difference between Pindar's Odes and Blake's Prophecies, is this:
if a Common Reader should do the hard work necessary to understand either, he would probably find
that he admired and enjoyed the Odes but not the
Prophecies. So at least I judge from my own experience, and that of many others not of the elect. And
in this is implied the answer to the other question:
How can you know when a book is very good? You
can't, not in the ways you can know the sky is blue
or the earth round. The surest you can be is for a
great many readers both common and aristocratic to
agree that it is good; when aristocrats alone like
it, as with the Odes and the Prophecies, about the
best you can do is to judge the tone with which they
speak to you of it; if the speaker is courteous and
seems to want you to share his enthusiasm, as Eliot
did when he wrote on Dante, trust him; but if he
is rude and seems contemptuous of you for being so
stupid, beware. If he concludes an essay as Winters
concluded the one I quoted earlier, beware.

> If my arguments are merely brushed aside, I shall win
> by default within twenty years. If I am right, there will
> be no great harm in this, and it will not be the first
> time I have won an argument in this manner; but if I am
> wrong, it will be unfortunate.[*]

The publishers of the first collection of Shakespeare's plays put the case well:

> From the most able, to him that can but spell: There you
> are number'd. . . . Reade him, and againe, and againe:
> and if then you do not like him, surely you are in some
> manifest danger, not to understand him.

Literature is a part of the Common Reader's life
—a part only, but of it—and it gives him power, and
confidence in his power, to communicate. He does

[*] *Function of Criticism,* p. 75.

not challenge those who know more than he; he gives way to those who have more energy than he; he is not contemptuous of those beneath him. Literature brings knowledge and it may bring wisdom, it may even instruct in virtue, it has changed a man's life more than once; it may divert you from trouble for a while like a game, it may untie your knots with laughter, it can purge you for a time of great dread, it has power if you will to elevate you to something like ecstasy. Yet, no matter how much pain literature may awaken in you—outrage you with images of violence like the *Iliad*, horrify you with Oedipus' gouged eyes, instruct you in the inmost ways of sin like Dante, rend from you inconsolable sobs like Lear's death, figure forth your most private inquietude like Dostoevsky—still it also produces delight, if only the delight of ordered thoughts and of language used well. Lovers are poets, and experience of literature is something like love: it quickens its lover to intense life, it is not everlasting but at the time it is of eternity, it is incalculably precious, its power is measured both by its delight and by its anguish, it is there for all who want it, each makes it himself. It is everybody's language shaped with love.

THE ANNEALING

She lived from day to day and didn't much care which day it was. If she laughed once or twice, laughed big that day, she had it made. If she cried more than she laughed, she knew it wasn't her day. Sometimes it wasn't her day, not really, for weeks on end. Sometimes, with that liquor sloshing around in her, it was her day, her night, her everytime.

One day Minnie D. and Olivia Santiago had a fight. Minnie was big, plump, easygoing, and golden brown. Olivia was black with purple shades and hated niggers anyway, scorning them with a proud look on her black Castilian face. She pushed all the time. Minnie D. was easygoing, a soft-laughing girl with seven children out of five fathers, and a dead or deserted husband posed stylishly in a Woolworth's gaudy frame. She had a lover, Leroy, who never laughed, and beat her for her Relief money twice a month. Olivia had six children. That morning she discovered she was pregnant again and would have to get the Supplementary Relief, and that entered her in that slut Minnie's class. She had a hard-working husband and she still couldn't make it and so she started the

fight. She passed Minnie's free-and-easy kind of door
with the two, three, malodorous garbage bags which
Minnie planned to bring down if she ever got to
leave sweet Leroy lying all manlike in the bed, not
caring that it was all adding to the three or so generations of stench accreting in the hallway. Olivia
yelled at Minnie through the door, telling her, "No-
good nigger get that garbage out of the hall," and
tiraded her about how that was what the niggers
were doing to honest, good people. And her Nelson,
he worked hard at the job and made the money, and
people like that, like that Minnie, they loused it up
for everyone. Minnie, screaming. "You no-good spic
bitch," came piling out of the door, wearing only a
white half-slip, her plump, round good nature gone,
her teeth bared, and her eyeball all yellow with
blood and hate. Olivia was thin, but she was full of
the great hate too.

They fought all the way down from the third floor
to the ground floor and boiled out into the street.
They pulled hair, twisted breasts; they bit, scratched,
screamed, drooled; they kicked; they gouged. The
neighbors came to the doors and stood, laughing
and shouting encouragement, picking sides. The kids
screamed with delight. One of Minnie's sons came
tearing up the street, leaving the little card game he
was playing in, to kick Olivia's oldest daughter in
the slats. Ramon, Olivia's oldest boy, had to be held
back from putting a flick-knife into this cool card
player, Alonso.

They fought their way out to the middle of the
street where, half naked, they tried to push one
another into a greasy pool of oily water, pulling,
snarling, while everyone stood around and said
things like, "I put five to four on that fine fat girl.
Man, look at her." Minnie, not laughing at all now,
her great breasts shining with sweat, her slip almost
gone, a few festive shreds holding on to the elastic
cutting into her soft brown middle, kept swatting
mightily. Olivia dodged, ducked, and kept trying to
close in so she could sink her bright white teeth into
Minnie's throat, or better, her breast. A joker, wear-

ing a motorcycle fly-boy cap with a white visor, stood behind the crowd and stopped traffic like a police-man, or a general. All the windows were opened and everybody was having a ball, looking out. Leroy, the lover, hung out, yelling, "Give her one, Minnie, give her one good, you hear?" laughing to beat every-thing, and that was the first time he had laughed in three weeks, not since he had scored in a poker game, scored in a craps game, scored with a little light-skin girl way up in Harlem, scored. Hinton, Minnie's middle boy, whereabouts of the father unknown, not since he was conceived, stood in the kitchen and contemplated knifing Leroy. He didn't have the nerve. He was nine years old.

Some do-gooder called the fuzzy bulls, and they came tearing around the corner, sounding the siren loud so everyone would know they were coming and could compose their little stories about they didn't know who, or what, or when. In that sunken Sump of Brooklyn by the Canal, everyone minds their business, Officer. The crowd scattered to the stoops and stood there like good little stupids, only seeing, peaceful, grinning because it was such a good fight. But Olivia and Minnie were in earnest and didn't hear a thing. Minnie, looking like a fat, good-natured hula dancer, swatted Olivia finally, catching her low and bringing on the miscarriage Olivia wanted so badly. If she hadn't felt so bad later, and her pride hadn't been hurt, she wouldn't have done a thing. The policemen stepped out of the car with that slow dignity they had, squaring their chests, hunching their shoulders, fingering their guns, swaggering as if to say, it will be your arse if anyone starts anything at all. The crowd fell silent, watching. Hard boys, cool boys, from the territory for miles around, had materialized on the rooftops and stood around, looking down into the streets innocently. The cops, they missed nothing at all.

"Who started it?" the cops asked. Minnie, panting and triumphant, shrugged her shoulders and said they were having a discussion that had gotten out of hand. Seeing that she had won and Olivia was

smeared, her clothes torn, her face bleeding, filthy
with oil and water, Minnie was inclined to laugh
about the whole thing. Olivia hated Minnie more,
but there were codes you never violated. Not there in
the Sump. "Come on, come on," one of the cops said
impatiently. The street became very still and the cops
knew what that meant. They were hated for breaking up a very prime battle. It was like taking away
red meat, chitterlings, a little cheap whiskey, or the
TV when everything else was gone. Minnie shrugged
and smiled an innocent smile, folded her arms, and
tried, with some degree of dignity, to cover her
vast breasts, which were exciting the men and boys
in the crowd, not to speak of the cops. No one said
anything, not even Olivia, and the cops told Minnie
D. they could run her in for indecent exposure, for
disturbing the peace, for any number of things.
Minnie whined she wasn't doing nothing, Officer, and
someone shouted, "Aw, let them alone," and Olivia
stated it was just the friendly, if somewhat athletic,
discussion between two friends. The cops, not caring
if the bastards killed one another, muttered threats,
told them all to go home, clear the streets before I
run you in, but knew that in the middle of such a
mob, running anyone in might be more trouble than
it was worth, considering no one was hurt. Minnie,
clapped on the back by a few of her kind of women,
who knotted around her to hide her gleaming naked-
ness, left the field of honor, beginning to forget
because it was past. Olivia, comforted by a few of
her friends, was bleeding from scratches, from the
nose, from her vagina. Her miscarriage had started.

Leroy, feeling full of fun, having enjoyed himself
thoroughly at the fight, gave Hinton the last of
Minnie D.'s Relief money, and told him to go and
bring a bottle of something good to drink, and not to
forget, or run off, or do anything wrong, you hear,
Boy? And before Hinton had even gone out the door,
he took Minnie and laid her on the bed to reward
her bitter, bitter life with a little something sweet
for victory's sake. Hinton lingered at the door,
watching, till the unbearable groans and moans and

screams started, and wished he had had the courage to stab Leroy when he had the chance.

Olivia, being bathed by her neighbors, chattered bitterly. When everyone had left, she sat down and wrote a revealing letter to the Relief people. She named names and stated facts, and even, in the heat of her burning, scorched pride, she overstated things. She wrote that Minnie beat her children and this was untrue. In fact, Minnie frequently interposed herself between Leroy's fists and the kids because she loved them. That kind of pain she could take, and did.

Mr. Jones, the Relief Investigator, came, responding to the complaint. Since it was not his normal time to visit, he came when Leroy was at home, lying half naked on the bed. Minnie D. told Mr. Jones that Leroy was a distant cousin and a good friend who sometimes stayed over. And when he stayed, he gave money for his food and brought little presents for the kids. Mr. Jones shook his head. Minnie was an old-time sore point with him. The kids stood around as they always did, not looking directly at the Investigator, but somehow managing to radiate hostility. It never even occurred to Hinton, wearing a torn shirt, and stinking, to see irony in what Minnie said about the presents Leroy brought for the kids. As for the oldest, Alonzo, he was too concerned about a rep with the boys, the clothes he bought out of stolen money, and his straightened, exquisitely marcelled hair. Alonzo and Leroy had a healthy contempt for one another. But no one was betraying, saying anything more to the Investigator other than that they needed money. The money grant wasn't enough. The complaint was a tissue of lies. Mr. Jones sighed. He had worked hard with Minnie, through "cousins" like Leroy. He had tried everything, all the proper social-work techniques and a few improper ones. Mr. Jones had threatened. He had pleaded. He had appealed to Minnie D. as one Negro to another. He resented that she lived a life apart, wild, bounded by *now,* sloppy, meaningless. He pointed to himself. His wife teaching. His two affordable and neat children. His little house in Queens. His sense of tomorrow. All that, all of it, could be Minnie's too. She just told him her troubles.

Over the years, it had been a case of not knowing or caring that there was tomorrow. Mr. Jones knew the tomorrows and the promise in store for the world of man when all the inequities would be righted. It was a matter of managing, cleaning, meeting deadlines, marrying, saving, keeping appointments, and bringing up the children with a sense of the future. He couldn't understand Minnie D.'s recurring fall from grace. She drank. She had lovers and had children. She spent her money on the wrong things. Bright, impermanent things interested her. If Leroy didn't get the Relief money first, it was fried chicken for a few days and little food thereafter, unless she didn't pay the rent or the utilities. Once, they cut off the lights, but she cheerfully tapped the meters. They had fought it down the years, irresponsibility and procedure, Mr. Jones and Minnie D. But this time, Mr. Jones knew they had come to the end of it. It had been arrests, Children's Court, Domestic Relations Court, Child Placement, Foster Homes, private agencies, the truant officer, the Bureau of Child Guidance, the Mayor's Committee on Multi-Problem Cases, the Society for the Prevention of Cruelty to Children, the Department of Health, the Department of Buildings, the Office of Rent Control, Visiting Nurses, Homemakers, memos, endless memos. But misspending Minnie D. was always getting a little drunk here and there, getting hurt, going to clinics, to this doctor, that chiropractor, and the other faith-healer, or spending it on one bright blue silk dress she wore on Saturdays for the big nights when she left the children in charge of Alonso, who tied them up, and went uptown with Leroy. Well, she needed to laugh, didn't she? Mr. Jones, he wouldn't understand.

Minnie wondered who had done this to her. Somehow she couldn't connect Olivia Santiago with something like that. It was a simple fight and everyone forgot, now that it was over. Mr. Jones was hurt, annoyed at the presence of Leroy, who looked sullen. His look seemed to say, don't ask me no questions, Boy. Mr. Jones, perspiring in his Ivy League suit, his striped rep tie a little askew, asked as few questions as possible and made notes in his little book.

When he returned to the office, Mr. Jones worried about finding a way out. "Close the case," the Supervisor glibly said. He couldn't bring himself to do that. She would be back, getting Relief, in no time flat. He had an idea. He would frighten her with the insane asylum. A new discussion with his Supervisor seemed to indicate, as they say, a psychiatric interview. Yes, perhaps, Mr. Jones thought, it would scare her. Very little else did. In order to get approval for a psychiatric interview, Mr. Jones had to state the case a little strongly. But after all, he reasoned, wasn't chronic irresponsibility a form of psychosis?

He wrote a letter to Minnie D., telling her to be home on a certain day, or he would surely close her case and cease Relief. And to make it certain, he scheduled the interview for Check Day. Minnie D. didn't mind and told Leroy he would have to be out of the house then. Leroy, who had come back after three days gone, was willing to be gone for three days more. He had the need of a fix and wanted money since there were no Relief funds left. Of course, Minnie D. wasn't going to tell that snotty Mr. Jones she had spent the money on Leroy, gambled just a little, gotten drunk and laughed a lot, bought Hinton a red tie, and herself a foundation and baby-blue suede pumps, and it would be another month at least till the electric company bothered her.

The psychiatrist was a woman named Ostreicher. She was a German refugee of the thirties who had kept on cultivating her accent, but to no avail. She had never been able to get an expensive clientele. She was unable to write any books. Every time she came up with a new theory that would perhaps revolutionize psychoanalysis, Karen Horney, Erich Fromm, or Wilhelm Reich wrote a book about it first.

She was bitter. She had to work for the city in order to make a good living.

She was perfectly on time at nine in the morning, and stood in the quiet sunlit street, littered from one end to the other, watching all the little children playing. She stood, waiting for Mr. Jones, a stolid, squat monolith in expensive tweeds. Her sturdy legs were stuck like the feet of conquerors into sensible English walking-shoes. Mr. Jones was ten minutes late and she was filled with hatred and loathing for the imperfect and incorrect Relief Department. When Mr. Jones appeared, she looked at him with contempt, feeling that somehow he didn't belong in those Ivy League clothes. One button of his button-down collar was undone. It seemed to her that Mr. Jones belonged with the clients. Because he was late, her day had already started badly.

Mr. Jones excused himself politely for being late. Dr. O. could not really accept it at all. She adjusted healthily to these things, of course, but she knew, being of the old Freudian school, that there were always the unconscious impulses. She asked Mr. Jones to fill her in on Minnie D. It seemed to her that Mr. Jones's memo was just a little too sparse. Neglect, irresponsibility, repetition of patterns—they were common things that were, true, neurotic, but not in and of themselves psychotic, you understand. Mr. Jones understood that. Of course, she, Dr. O., was glad to examine the woman. But then, wasn't it a waste of taxpayers' money if there were no bases of commitment? Mr. Jones hemmed a little, and hawed, and became committed under the stern, disapproving stare of the doctor. He had another thing to blame Minnie for. He tried to meet the Doctor halfway. He had had courses in psychology. He talked in very learned terms about the refusal to ventilate problems, hostility patterns, destructive patterns, recurrence of the death wish in the shape of the dead, the deserted husband, the five putative fathers, the Leroy-figure, long, black, lean and saturnine, who was capable, in equal parts on equal days, of largess or destruction. He beat the

children. All the casuals who tramped in and out of
Minnie's life beat the children. They were a noisome,
smelly lot. And then, didn't it follow, because Minnie
placed herself in those situations where she was
permissive of the beatings, the neglect, the hunger,
that she accepted, condoned, approved in effect? So
he told Dr. O. that she did beat the children. Dr. O.
nodded her head approvingly, noting everything
Mr. Jones had to say. When he had finished, Mr.
Jones was sweating a little.

He led the Doctor up the stairs, past all the paint-
cracked doors, past and up the stairs through wells
tilted crazily, ready to collapse everything to the
bottom, past the numberless doors where the mad
mambo music poured out, the sullen-sad jazz singers
sung their blues of living, and through the great
banal beat of the morning soap operas coming in
on the T.V. They passed the little stenchy cubicles
shared by two families to a floor, and the graffiti
gratuitously graven onto the walls, obscening the
world and telling it, them, those, the fuzz, and everyone to go and . . . Outside Minnie's door, the light
bulb had burned out, and the hallway was a pool
of black limned with little lights where the cracks
under the doors showed. Mr. Jones lit a match for
Dr. O. to find her stolid way, stepping over the
shards of lives, the dust, the dirt, the grainy grease,
and avoiding the garbage bags Minnie hadn't gotten
around to bringing down. In the sputter of the going-
out match, they saw, emblazoned in unseen red,
Minnie D.'s lipstick, Hinton's little rebellion. "Fuck
Leroy," it said, and if ever the landlord got around
to putting a bulb in the hallways, Hinton or some
other one of Minnie D.'s kids was going to be
whopped. They could hear the big booming sound
of a radio coming out of Minnie D.'s door and her
contralto singing a swinging song, full of life, full
of today's happiness. It was Friday, the check was
coming, and she had a little something out of the
left-over bottle Leroy thought he had hidden. They
were going to go out that night and none of the
children was sick for once. Only the minor little

cloud of Mr. Jones, looming no larger than a punitive
fist on the horizon, was coming that morning. Today
she had a little future and that was tonight. She
didn't much care what followed tonight, only that
she drank, she danced, she got loved by Leroy, and
slept very soundly indeed.

She was wearing only a pure-white slip when she
answered the door, and her skin glowed dark and
rich brown. Plump against it they could see the
counterpoint of brown skin, the breast and belly
lines, the emphasis of the large, lazy, child-caring
nipples, and the black pubic triangle. She had been
seen by Mr. Jones, to his great discomfort, like this
before. Minnie D. let them in. Dr. O. followed
steadily, smelling everything out. When they saw
the Doctor's face, they all stiffened because the in-
audible alarm note went out. The children stood
around, clean as Minnie felt she ought to get them,
sullen and resentful, not looking at the newcomers,
staring everywhere else, or at one another, or reading torn comic books. Only Hinton looked at them,
wishing he had stabbed Leroy, wondering if he could
take a knife and stab everyone in sight, especially
now his mother-slut, Minnie D., dressed in her pure-
white slip and naked underneath. Alonso, the oldest,
the cool poker player, sat, impeccably wearing his
gang uniform: white shoes, white pants, a blue Ivy
League Paisley-print shirt, a stocking on his head
to keep his marcel in perfect wavy form. Sitting
aloofly, Alonso, on a three-legged kitchen chair with
a bongo between his legs, kept up a constant little
subliminal mutter like distant, dangerous drums.
The youngest caterwauled in his crib and the radio
boomed the bouncy, swinging accompaniment to
what Minnie had been singing when they knocked.

Mr. Jones did the honors, telling Minnie D. that
Dr. Ostreicher was really Miss Ostreicher, a social
worker wishing to ask a few questions for a survey.
Minnie D. regretted that she had only bothered to
clean the kitchen, where Mr. Jones usually did the
interviewing. Dr. O., standing there, looked them
all over and knew immediately that it was a family

beyond hope, beyond redemption. She looked at the soft brown skin of Minnie glowing delectably around and under the pure-white slip. "Put on your clothes," she snapped. Minnie D., trying to be pleasant because she was still on tonight's dust of having a ball, smiled at the hard, square-faced lady and said, "Won't you sit down?" Mr. Jones skittered a little over the floor, trying to adjust the kitchen chairs for everyone, and caught the hard, look-at-you-there-man contempt look of Alonso, who muttered the drums derisively. A roach scuttled across the floor, banana-peel bound. Miss O. said that she was Dr. O., not a social worker at all, and that she had come to examine Minnie D., and to put on some clothes. She cracked it out in her hard, let's-get-things-clear voice so that everyone shut up, even Alonso. He stopped the drum mutter against this hard, hard authority and tried to look cool and insolent, and make me, man; but she had. Minnie, not understanding what it was all about, smiled painfully, starting to come down out of her dream, and went into the other room to find something she could put on over the pure-white silk slip. "What I need a doctor for, Mr. Jones?" she called in her whiny voice from the other room. "Nothing wrong with me at all. I have my health, praise the Lord." Mr. Jones looked at Dr. O. as if to say, was that necessary? But, taking in the implacable, methodical face; the hard, square shoulders bunched up in the rough and ready cloth; the thick thighs curving through the rough skirt; the gray stockings—he knew it was necessary. He was a little ashamed to have been bested in front of the children, especially Hinton, whose disturbed confidence he had succeeded in winning with bright bribes of candy.

Dr. O. took out a notebook and put it on the table. She tapped a little silver pencil and waited, uncaring in the ring of hostile dark faces. She appeared to listen to the sounds of morning coming in through the alleyway windows. She watched a hard bar of untrammeled sunlight blasting onto the floor, shining on the caked cracks between the boards. She picked

up a little silver vase on the table, containing dusty,
artificial flowers, looked casually underneath, and
saw Hotel Something-or-Other written on it. She
put it down and gave a look of triumph to Mr. Jones,
which was understood by everybody but Mr. Jones.
"Get these children out of here," she told Minnie D.
when she came in, compromising with propriety by
wearing a tan, stained skirt, leaving her breasts un-
bound, and bouncing softly, rustling in white silk
under Dr. O.'s avid, hating stare. Minnie D., trying
to hold on to the remnants of a smile, shooed them
all out, even Hinton, who never went outside at all.
Alonso took off his stocking with careful insolence
and slouched out, every line of his body, his neat
clothes, saying, do me something, man, do me something. "Whew," Minnie D. said when they had all
trooped outside, "raising a family is sure hard
work," and smiled a propitiatory smile.

"No one told you to have so many children," Dr. O.
said. "Could you turn off the radio and get the
infant quiet?"

Minnie D. could feel something unreasonable
forming inside her. Her cunning mind was good
enough to tell her that there was something more
to this whole bit. Mr. Jones had always been
friendly, making his fusses about keeping clean and
getting rid of Leroy. But the hard-faced lady with
the icy eyes that kept looking at her in some certain
way—she meant a little more. And when Minnie
felt that way, she began to close herself up, get the
look on her face that said nothing at all, answered
sassy because they wanted something from her she
didn't understand. She tried to get Leroy out of her
mind.

"Put something on," Dr. O. told her. "You are
indecent."

Minnie D. shuffled to turn off the radio, to find a
blouse, to come back slowly to the metronomic ticking Dr. O. made with her little silver pencil to mark
Minnie's movements.

"What you have a doctor here for?" she asked Mr.
Jones.

"It's Central Office's idea," Mr. Jones told her, somehow caught and unable to say too much, ashamed because no one was acting very nice and he didn't know what to do about it. Two buttons of her blouse remained open, for spite.

"What day is it?" Dr. O. asked Minnie D., snapping out her question as if to say, why are you so evil, why are you so resistant? Minnie D. just looked at her as if to ask, what is your bit, why come on so salty? She didn't know. They bugged her more. She didn't bother to answer this silly, silly question at all. It was Check Day. Who need know any more? She looked coolly at the Doctor. The Doctor nodded. The interview was going along satisfactorily. "You don't know what day it is?" she asked Minnie D., looking at the deep cleft where the spiteful buttons didn't button, and at the way her haunches strained against the tan skirt.

"I know what day it is," Minnie D. told the Doctor.

"You do?" the Doctor said with benign hatefulness, nodding with the proper degree of meaningful gesture, and wrote this in the book too. Mr. Jones, writhing inside to see it happen this way, poured his calm oil on the water. "Mrs. D., tell the lady what she asks for. She is on your side."

Minnie D., seeing the hard eyes take her apart and leave her nothing at all, knew this witch was never on anyone's side. "April 18th," she said, packing contempt into those little words. The Doctor was a little ahead of her and finessed Minnie D. by interpreting attitude. Then they relaxed for a little silence while the Doctor looked around the room with hate, with loathing, with don't touch me. Those sensible shoes under the heavy feet moved swiftly and crushed a roach making advances. "Where did you get this?" she asked with a policeman's triumph, holding up the little silver vase and spilling one red cardboard rose onto the greasy checked linoleum. Minnie looked sullen and shrugged it off.

"Why are you asking me these questions?" she asked.

"Where did you get this?" the Doctor asked and made minute notes on minute reactions. Minnie D. feared what the Doctor wrote in her little notebook. She could almost feel the happiness slip away completely, almost irretrievably, and feel the blackness come down on her, down like depression, down like candy and sweets and liquor taken away. She thought she could hear the rattle of the letter boxes being opened up and everyone crowing with satisfaction. They had made it for another two weeks without discovery, pulling out the window envelopes, hearing the satisfying rustle of cellophane ripping, holding their checks. It came drifting up the stairs. It was a feeling like dancing in the streets. All that laughing. And the shopkeepers rubbed hands because it was payday, and eager liquor-store people looked out, welcoming from behind their just-ordered cartons of whisky. And she felt a little sad, left out. She had to go down and get her check too. But she didn't hear what the Doctor said, only coming back to the little scene to see the Doctor writing it all down, whatever was asked and not answered. Client, having obviously stolen the vase, avoids all mention of it. Blocks out, blanks out, mild catatonic state, stares into space, has difficulty focusing attention. "What did you say?" she asked. Mr. Jones, the spirit of help, wondering how they had gotten this psychiatrist, started to ask the question again. Dr. O. stopped him with a gesture. "How much is five and six?" she asked Minnie D., sounding like talking-down-to, and treating Minnie D. like a child. Minnie D. was stung a little this time. "I'm no child," she said.

"And that depends on how you answer the questions," Dr. O. said with galling sweetness. They sat for a while, quiet. Minnie D. struggled with it. It was all different from dealing with Mr. Jones. When Mr. Jones tried to come on hard and asked his penetrating questions, she whined a little and cunningly, shrewdly avoided all pitfalls because she had been playing this game for so long a time. But she could sense that she had gotten off on the wrong foot with this hard lady and this lady was going to put her down hard or break a gut trying. She wondered what she had done to antagonize this lady. Here was a menace. The worst kind. She could see it. She could hear it. She could smell it. She knew it. She should play the good client and answer the questions, whine where she should whine about how hard times were and how hard it was to manage and how hard it was to bring up children, and know nothing else about anything. She knew what the Doctor was doing with her, but she couldn't help herself. She was beginning to play it as the Doctor wanted, play it to lose her head, play it with a little dignity, and the dignity of it was going to cost her the check and the night with Leroy. "I'm no child," she told the Doctor again.

Dr. O., with infinite and cunning patience, asked how much nine and five were, what day it was, did she hear strange voices? Was it winter, was it summer, what season of the year was it anyway, and how did she care for her children? Minnie D. drove herself out of her dream of tonight, her sleepwalk of now, and weighing all the factors, answered the Doctor. But she couldn't fight the black tide of anger that welled up inside her the way it had with Olivia Santiago. She answered the questions sullenly, so sullenly, and the Doctor wrote not only what she said, but how she said it. Mr. Jones began to feel it building up like angry crowds gathered in the dusty streets staring down the cops, or like the boys, leaning in their white, white pants on the corner and waiting for the action. Who knew? The action might be you any time. He knew. He saw what Dr. O. apparently didn't see. But that Dr. O., it didn't matter to her one way or another. She had looked upon the soft brown Minnie-flesh and she was disturbed. She had seen the sullen faces of Minnie D.'s children, the rotting building, the shouting and singing in the halls, the littered streets, the pervading smell of the nearby canal choked with garbage and dead flesh, the little silver vase with the artificial flowers marked Hotel Something-or-Other, and the helpless face of Mr. Jones, quick to jump to conclusions of neurosis and psychosis. She wasn't going to be stopped. Not Dr. O.

Minnie D. sat there, not looking at Dr. O., not even facing her, but looking away, yet sort of, toward, out of her shrewd peripheral vision, seeing it all and knowing it all. But that basic wisdom of hers was robbed by so many hungers and by the dream of tonight and Leroy. The timelessness of life, the ball tonight with this half-month's stipend, the thought of that check sitting there in the mailbox itched her as if she were tickled, or fingered. And what if that sweet rat, Leroy, sneaked back, took the check as he had before, forged it, and went out and had himself a ball, leaving Minnie with her squalling brood? Surely one of the neighbors would come in and give her a drink out of pity and good spirits, but what was that compared to a ball anyway? She sat there in her tweed, Dr. O. did, and was unrelenting and harsh and every time she spoke, she got Minnie D.'s back up so she could feel hair pricklings at the base of her spine, and all the way up to the nape of her neck.

She kept muttering, "Talking to me that way, like I was my bitty child, Hinton. I ain't no child," while Dr. O. kept obligingly putting it down, and she said challengingly to the Doctor, "Put that down in your little book. I ain't no child."

"Now, Mrs. D.," Mr. Jones said. But she kept up with her dangerous mutter.

"Is that the way the children are always dressed?" Dr. O. asked.

"What's the matter with the way my children are dressed?" Minnie asked, stung again. "What do you expect me to do with the little money the Relief gives me?"

"Now, Mrs. D.," Mr. Jones said, "you know that this is all I'm entitled to give you." She kept up the muttering. "And anyway, you have misspent the money so many times," he reminded her. "And what about Leroy?"

"Where did you steal this?" Dr. O. asked.

Minnie D. rose, angered almost beyond endurance,

and screamed, "I didn't steal this." Leroy had given her this little present, together with the little clutch of paper flowers so cunningly and artfully painted like the real thing. Well, she thought, maybe Leroy had not gotten it the right way. But her man was a little like a child, meaning no harm, like her sulky Hinton, perhaps, or like her Alonso. And if the truth were known, there were more roaming the street who were worse, much worse. She didn't say this. She said, "If you keep on talking that way, I'll throw you out." But, she saw that if she went after Dr. O., she would get her hide whipped. Dr. O. was no Olivia Santiago, but she had shoulders like a man, legs like a man, and big hands that could handle her easily. She was a little afraid.

Minnie D. started for the door. "Where are you going, Mrs. D.?" Mr. Jones asked.

"I'm going to get my check," she said because she couldn't control herself, thinking about it down there in the rusted mailbox, tortured for it. "Sit down, Mrs. D.," Mr. Jones said. She started to explain the possibility of the check being stolen.

"Sit down," Dr. O. told her. "I am not finished with you." She opened her little black doctor's bag and took out a stethoscope. "Strip to the waist," she told Minnie D. Mr. Jones stood up to go into the next room. "You don't have to go," Dr. O. told Mr. Jones.

"I'm not taking off my clothes while there's a man here," said Minnie D. to the Doctor.

"Do as I tell you."

"Look, I'll go into the other room," Mr. Jones said. The Doctor shrugged her shoulders as if to say, what did it matter, and smiled her contempt for Mr. Jones, who kept hopping from one leg to the other. He went into the doorless other room and stood by the window, looking out, studying the depressing back alleys, seeing white rags fluttering on the clotheslines, pigeon flocks, kids climbing up and down the fences, a scene of domestic tragedy taking place in another window. A man was beating his wife silently and she got beaten without screaming.

With insolent grace, Minnie D. took off her blouse, slipped the shoulder straps off, and stood, half-naked, in front of Dr. O. She was a splendid savage, warm and defiant brown, big-breasted, full-breasted, her face frozen with black, sullen dignity. Dr. O. jabbed the silver weapon of her icy stethoscope between her breasts, making Minnie's skin goosepimple. Minnie jumped a little and lost that splendid, defiant look. Wielding the forever icy tip of the stethoscope, unconcerned, Dr. O. pushed, jabbed, probed, listened, and felt Minnie here and there, her hateful white hands prying over Minnie's body till she was ready to scream. Does this bother you and does that bother you and if Minnie answered with her voice full of obvious hate, the silver tip flickered out to touch her and make her shiver in punishment. Then Minnie sat while the Doctor whaled her with a rubber mallet to test her reflexes, hurting her a little, the way she used it. "Do you drink? Take drugs? Given to sleeping too much? Have sleepless nights? Special troubles when you menstruate? How often do you masturbate? Dream? Don't dream? And how many times a week do you have sex with men? With women?" the Doctor asked, seeming not to care about the answers while she listened, tapping, toying with the silver vase, making Minnie jumpy, so that sometimes she answered without thinking and had to retract what she said. The Doctor took it all down, sitting there, pin-neat and mechanical, clean and well dressed, untouched by the stink of cooking greens and baby piss and deodorant. Minnie, who had never worried about it too much, sat there, half nude, finding that her uncontrollable hands and arms tended to cover herself up in the face of that long long stare the Doctor stared at her. "Come back, Mr. Jones," the Doctor called. Minnie struggled to raise her slip, put on her blouse, was fumbling around, clumsy, entangled in straps, cloth, and her own flesh. Mr. Jones saw and turned away as if he had overlooked something new in the fascinating, true-life scene being played out across the alleyway.

Seeing how Minnie struggled with the blouse, Dr. O. wrote down that she had poor motor responses.

And before Minnie finished buttoning up, the Doctor asked again where she was, what city, what borough, what district, what planet, lashing her with questions, and did she beat her children? She played with the silver vase and let another flower fall to the floor, and Minnie kept getting more nervous. She tried a digression. "Why are you picking on me?" she asked the Doctor. "Why are you white folks against me?"

"But I'm not white." Mr. Jones said.

The Doctor didn't bother to answer, it being obvious to everyone, even to Mr. Jones, abstracted in his back yard, that being picked on was a delusion of Minnie's. She put it down. Paranoid delusion. Thinks she is not being helped by the Relief people and is being picked on by the Doctor who is, if anything, benign beyond belief. Ascribes it to racial prejudice. Accuses dark Mr. Jones of this too. Mr. Jones, feeling that everything was all right now, came back into the room and stood behind Minnie, leaning against the soiled stove.

And the Doctor started it again, asking questions sweetly this time, asking them with a let's-humor-her kind of patience that no one missed, not Minnie, not Mr. Jones. Minnie, she couldn't play it anyway because she knew that final flood of anger was going to come up, up, up in her and she was going to have to try and hit, kill that woman.

"It has come to our attention that you beat the children," Doctor O. said. Minnie said it was untrue. Minnie said she might hit them to keep them in line. Every mother did that. She never beat them. The Doctor looked at her for a second, and almost abstracted, hefted the silver vase a little bit with a questioning look on her face. Minnie, unable to take it any more, knocked it out of her hand. It fell, silver to the floor, scattering the paper flowers and a little water one of the children had put into it to make them grow. "Don't go bugging me," she screamed. "What you trying to do to me?"

"Nothing at all. Nothing at all," the Doctor said softly, looking like hit me, try and hit me. They sat there, silent, Mr. Jones horrified, not knowing what to do. "Did you think," the Doctor asked, "that those flowers would grow in that water?" Minnie couldn't even laugh at such a stupid question any more because the Doctor had wound her up too much. "If you don't get her out of here, something bad is going to happen," she told Mr. Jones. "Why don't you answer me?" the Doctor asked, softening the harshness of her low, hoarse voice. Minnie got up, went to the kitchen drawer, and pulled out one long bread knife and appealed to Mr. Jones: "Get her out of here." The Doctor sighed slowly, stood up, put everything into the little black medical bag, snapped it neatly to, buttoned the top button of her jacket, and said, "Let us go, Mr. Jones," and walked out.

Mr. Jones smiled weakly at Minnie D. and followed Dr. O. out into the hallway. He followed her down the stairs and to the front door. She turned and blocked him from the street, holding him there in the rancid hallway. "You were right, Mr. Jones." He couldn't seem to understand her. "She is obviously paranoid. We will have to commit her," Dr. O. told Mr. Jones.

"But . . ."

"I will write out the commitment papers for you. You will go back. I will send for an ambulance. And, oh, yes, the police."

"But . . ."

She took out a pad of commitment forms and began to write: "potentially dangerous . . ." Mr. Jones saw. "You drove her to it," he told Dr. O. Dr. O. looked at him. Under her pale eyes, he could only perspire and hate Minnie for what she had made him do. Dr. O. reached out suddenly and her thick hand quickly buttoned his undone collar. He felt the tip of her pencil touch his chin. Dr. O. kept looking at him and continuing to write a breviary of disturbances. Feeble hatred shook him. Dr. O. was beyond hatred. She tore, with a neat, ripping sound, three copies. One for him. One for the ambulance attendant. One she kept for herself. "Go up and wait for them to come." He turned and went back up the stairs. The wood creaked, ripping slowly loose from the walls.

They sent two policemen as a precaution till the ambulance came. The policemen stood around and looked at the patient suspiciously, fingering their nightsticks. They were ready to move fast because you never know how strong these looneys get when they blow their corks. Minnie D., bewildered, sat between them, not knowing what was wrong. The policemen noticed the fallen vase, the spilled water, an overturned chair, the implied violence, and watched her, making pleasant conversation with Mr. Jones. Minnie D. kept muttering over and over again, "What did I do?" When the boys in white came, dragging, as a matter of course, a strait jacket, she blew her top completely and jumped Mr. Jones, who was trying to tell her that everything would be all right if she kept calm. His tie was torn loose, his Ivy League suit was ripped, and she made a deep, bloody scratch up the side of his face. Like two accomplished pikemen lazily practicing their art, the police, dispassionately, almost sorrowfully, hit Minnie D. right and left, knocking her one way, catching her with the other nightstick to bounce her back, so that she bled bloody sideburns down both sides of her face. As she dropped, the attendants dressed her like a bad little child in a long, confining strait jacket. They sackmealed her down the stairs, her head drooping and bouncing on each tread, blood coming down on the steps. She screamed again and again and again. Leroy, who saw it all, wisely waited until they were gone and went to collect the Relief check to ball it up that night. He accepted. Mr. Jones went around to collect the children to place them in institutions and foster homes.

Minnie D., she lived it from day to day and almost cared what day it was because they were going to observe her for ten days and if she was good, they would have to say she is sane and let her go. But she looked around at the looneys, whom she was not

like, remembered Dr. O. and Mr. Jones, and the way
the policemen clobbered her right and left, and
wondered about the children and Leroy, who had
certainly taken all the money and spent it on drinks
and some slut up in Harlem. Had a ball on her money
while her children were there, everywhere, and she
was here without reason, falsely accused. So she kept
blowing her top whenever they talked to her. She
couldn't feel it ahead for ten days to play it cool,
because there is only *now*.

And in ten days, it was still now, and they put
her away in the state bin for another six months,
away from all the goodies, except for a little smug-
gled-in liquor she worked off in one way or another.
And in time, how bad can it be? The anger died
slowly and she whined to the doctor that she was
all right again, she will be good, she had done
wrong, which is most of all what they wanted to
hear. They let her out in six months; they gave her
back her children; they found her an apartment in
another part of the Sump district. Leroy heard she
was out, found her, and they set up housekeeping
again. He beat her at checktime and gave her the
kind of loving she needed, and in nine months, she
had another Hinton-baby.

Song

Who will recall my burberry
in the heaven of the shelvadors?
my input of marron, orlon, sirloin
in the great disposall?
my V8, hifi, tv, 3D
in the grand viyella?
No one.
Neither snow, nor rain, nor boxed britannica
shall stay that courier.
He will come.

Richard G. Stern

GARDINER'S legacy

Gardiner lived and died in such obscurity that the revelations of the last twenty years seem particularly, if somewhat peculiarly, vivid. And now that Mrs. Gardiner is dead, one wonders whether the revelations were peculiar in a way which will affect our view of her great work. The textbooks have it that she was a simple woman inspired to great deeds by two things, the loving memory of her husband, and a heroic commitment to history and literature. Who can say now? One knows that she began almost immediately after the funeral—if one can use a word which suggests a far more complex ceremony than Gardiner enjoyed. At any rate, it couldn't have been more than a month after the city put him in the earth that the news of the first two posthumous volumes appeared in the *Times*. And then, within six months, she'd found *Weatherby's Version* packed away with the old clothes in the attic, and Gardiner vaulted from the status of a footnote in the second edition of Spiller and Thorpe to someone who rated a chapter alongside James and Melville and Faulkner.

That first year, it looked somehow unnatural, a hoax of some sort. Someone even suggested that Elinor had written the new stuff herself. (As far as I was concerned, all the better. More would have been forthcoming while she lived.) But such suspicion couldn't last long, and didn't. Elinor was, well, no fool, but nothing could have tapped Weatherby from her, let alone the journals and letters. No woman born of woman could have written it, at least no woman whose imaginative power did not equal, say, Sappho's plus Jane Austen's. And no one has yet accused Elinor of imagination. What was there she saw, and saw well, which makes the final discovery even stranger.

There she sat in the midst of it, twenty years of brilliant commemoration, copying, collating, editing, managing the swelling estate, selecting playwrights and producers for the adaptations, corresponding with translators, scholars, devotees, newspaper people, a mammoth job, an enterprise that amounted to several millions of dollars, and more, of course, to a new image of action, character, and life.

For that's what Gardiner turned out to be, a Stendhal, a Dostoevsky, someone who'd hacked a new way to clarity, built new organs of sensibility and pumped them with air and blood. And there she was, giving it birth in the very act that betrayed her. Every commemorative motion, every discovery, ripped off her skin and flesh, broke the bones, ground them down, and blew the dust into space—and there she sat, getting photographed next to the bookshelves, apparently blooming, intact.

Can she really have remembered him? Certainly the man she discovered was not the one she'd known, had lived with forty years. Surely he must have seemed like someone out of a dark age and she a literary archeologist stumbling upon and then recovering the singular preservation. But forty years is forty years, and she'd never had anything but him. Hatched in some Dakotan province, pushed into Bismarck and then Milwaukee, slaving like a *fellaheen* to keep flesh to bone, seeing nobody, read-

ing nothing, hardly dreaming one gathered, and
then, at nineteen, meeting the unlikely boy ushering
in the movie theater—and that was it, until she was
sixty and began reading what had happened in the
interim. Happened while she kept him alive working
in the twenty cities that they lived in, clerking in
stores and offices and markets, money-changer in the
subways, elevator operator, waitress, railway
checker. A long list, now more or less immortal
with the rest of it.

And he writing, occasionally with luck, with
money, so that it wasn't always grind. She did see
half the world, although twice the local embassies
had to bail them out. (It's been reported that once
in Rome she prostituted for him, but this sort of
thing will only come out from now on, now that they
have finally stuffed her into a monument next to the
corpse of whoever it was they decided was Gardiner.)

Apparently she did the jobs and everything else
with relish. He was always, almost always, "nice"
to her. Which of course makes it worse. Years ago,
on some television interview, she said, "We never
quarreled. He was astonishingly acute about my feelings and always knew how to adapt his mood to
mine, to work a harmony. I would have done, I did
do everything I could for him because it was precisely what I wanted to do. His will was my will.
And yet I don't think that he mastered me as
Catherine Blake was mastered by William." (She
was almost a learned woman a few years after their
marriage. That was something else she got from
him.) "I was never his instrument. On the contrary,
he completed me, or made me feel complete, made
me, I believe, a real person, and, if you'll forgive a
possible blasphemy, I had never existed before. He
created me." A typical utterance. And this after she
had taken the measure of his loathing, knew how he
detested her spirit and her flesh, mocked at her with
his women, put her remarks into the most disgusting
mouths in modern letters, knew that he kept her
around him as a reminder of Hell (he capitalized it,

for he turned out to be a kind of secular theologian, if one may risk the contradiction). There she was for forty years, "the hair shirt," "the Adversary and the Primal Sin in one," these a couple of less picturesque and vehement examples of his view of her. All of which now appear in the last work of his she put her hand to, the three volumes of his *Elinor,* as she called it, the thousand pages of his loathing drawn from forty years of reflection. Drawn by her from journals, stories, and the first drafts of letters —"He never paid a bill without making a draft of it first," she joked about him once—most of which were indicated in the earlier volumes by the once mysterious "E" followed by asterisks. The most fantastic of all posthumous exhibitions. Consider the sheer bulk of his hatred. Apparently, he had written about her from the beginning, from the very first meeting. "A lump of dung in the lobby": this the gallant initial entry. He married her "to marry Lilith," and he called the union "the marriage of Heaven and Hell." Perhaps this is what made her speak of Blake. Yes, I suppose that one could trace her public utterances and find that every noble sentiment had been triggered by reading some viciousness of his. There are numerous examples, although systematic study of them would be work for a tough-minded man.

It'll be done, as will everything else to resurrect that barbarous union. Gardiner and his wife will turn on the spit in history as they never did in life. Every pounding which he never gave her will be given, and every one she suffered after, because she never suffered them directly, will be given too. Yes, like Stendhal and Dostoevsky, he will live next to his works, a sample of conduct as rigorous as a saint's, if dedicated to obscurer ends. One must marvel at him, the superb restraint which never once revealed its source.

One wonders of course about much of their married life. That they had no children doesn't matter. The notebooks tell us what children were to him. (It's reasonably clear that he forced at least ten of the women to have abortions.) The sexual life, however, undoubtedly proceeded on normal lines—whatever it meant to him, and what it meant was in the nature of research. (The chapter "In the Adversary," from his version of Crébillon's *Sopha,* may be consulted here.) As much as we know—and we know a great deal about the sheer domesticity of their lives, about their bed and bathroom, the kitchen table, incidents with carpets and toothpaste, walks, swims, shopping, all transformed by him into malicious vision—we will never really know what it was like. Fifteen thousand days they spent together, or fourteen say, when one discounts the excursions with his women, his eighty-six women, the already famous gallery of his amours, the women who composed a wholly different universe of delights, the forty women of his Purgatory, the forty-six of his Heaven —yes, he was the oddest of American lovers. It will not be so great a surprise if some of these partners deliver up attics of material to feed the mills of curiosity for another half century.

But no material will ever mean what Elinor's has meant; none will draw up the fog which must forever, I suppose, obscure her contribution. Every penetration of that fog reveals a different structure. It is as if this was what he calculated from the start.

Or could it possibly have been her scheme? One can hardly credit it, but what else explains so much that is dark now, her amazing ignorance of the others, of his true feelings, his immense perversity, she who saw so much so clearly. Elinor was a brilliant human being. Her reconstruction of his work alone marks her a startlingly able scholar, an editor and bibliographer of enormous knowledge, acumen, and sensitivity, an immensely able woman of affairs, a powerful and subtle diplomat. And all this is as nothing when one estimates the emotional complexity behind this mastery. So great is this complexity that I have wondered if it might not have been there from the beginning.

Is it possible that she was the great mover all

along, that she made him *living* as she later made
his legend? Who discovered whom in the lobby of
that theater? What did she bring with her from the
Dakotan plain, what instruments to have managed
so huge a legacy?

She did not write the books, nor the journals and
letters. No, but the universe within which they were
written, did she not provide that, shape that? And
did he perhaps see her rightly all along? "In the
Adversary." Was his work perhaps as much report
as image? This is the oddest mystery of the legacy.

THE STREET-CRIERS

A crow-black man with golden teeth came singing
Corpses, corpses,
one-a-dollar, two-a-dollar, corpses, nice ripe corpses
for sale,
I drive no hard bargains, don't cheat, dirt-cheap,
put aside your boxes, boxes,
boxes full of cake-mix, ketchup, cathodes, commenta-
tors, cowboys,
comestibles and potables—here's portable corrupti-
bles for sale!
Wormless, germless, sanitary-packaged, visible in
cellophane, bloodless, guaranteed
drained;
a necrophilic wonderland, a certainty of thrill-
shock (Pure Food and Drug Laws faith-
fully maintained).
I bring you logical conclusions, not just cadavers,
convicts and derelicts, disreputes and
prostitutes,
but philosophers of note! men who had a vote—not
just for presidents, commissioners of
sewers,

professional parishioners and practicing ruers—
men who were Doers! directors of boards of Tell
     and Tell! who told and told, and lived
     to be old;
I wheel them in my barrow, fresh at the marrow,
     and I sell them without sorrow, probably
     today but surely
     tomorrow,
corpses, corpses, I've corpses for sale, some of them
     are hearty, most of them are hale (some
     of them were criminals,
     but none of them in jail).

Came a man white as kleenex with clarabella nose-
     holes, clapperclaw voice-cords, bee-syrup
     spit: yowled Hot, oh hot,
     oh get them hot, babies, babies,
heterosexual human males, uniform as unicorns, hot
     from the hospitals (municipal, proprie-
     tary), steaming
     from the labor-tables' stirrups,
cursed from birth with inheriting the earth (simple
     in fee but liable for rent); then buy
     them, breed them,
     feed them, beat them, cart them, seat them in
     parliament;
babies, babies, born of wives, shards of women alive
     and dead, some of them wed, half of
     them mad and half of them sane,
     and all of them in woman's pain;
rear them to be saints, raise them to be shamans,
     bring them up for crooks or demons,
     tame them, lame them,
     make a Dalai Lama or Baal-shem-tov,
     Bodhisattva Buddha or Death-for-Love,
babies for space-ships, armies, navies, babies for
     diseases of ladies of the evening, for
     tetanus and typhoid,
     trouble with kidneys, trouble with thyroid,
     itches in the balls,
     gall-stones, stitches in the ribs,
     inflammation of the prostate, the bladder's

collapse both mild and severe,
the heart's nadir,
the cigarette lung and palsy in the tongue,
hot oh hot, oh get them while they're hot, take them
to the zoo and the Statue of Liberty, take
them to the lunatic museum
and the Natural History, to the pulp-paper mill
and the factory for pills and the circus of ills,
educate them
for democracy and serpasil;
for sale, for sale, babies male, and see, a premium
for each I willingly supply, free, free,
a warranty for puberty
(so if left on the beach they will not multiply).
Then get them while they're hot, before all the box-
tops rot, and the tropics turn to ice,
and the premiums are not
without their price.

ENVOY

The river round this island flows,
habitual fleas gnaw at the rose,
and up and down the barrowman goes.
The anarchist breaks our status quos,
and shrieks because there fall no blows,
no cataclysm,
and no danger;
only the usual clangor
of his anarchistic catechism
delivered in languor.
Here change would be a stranger
more alien than anger.
So up and down the barrowman ploys,
crying corpses, peddling boys.
This is why the graves
are empty of knaves.
This is why infants are thieved
from the wards.
This is why the sheaths are barren
of swords.

Memoirs of a

RUSSOPHILE

1

Believe me, this Exhibition is the merest of pretexts.
If it had not been a *Russian* exhibition, I would
have been bored stiff; I would not have gone; I
certainly wouldn't be writing about it. It's not that
I don't find America fascinating (or Tanganyika or
British Honduras). I do, particularly, in my country, the architecture of factories; the barely visible
structures of the past along railroad rights-of-way;
the districts in the big cities that have nothing but
human life to recommend them; towns like Solon,
Iowa, that are like movie sets struck after a B
Western; and the varieties of dignity and indignity
that are required to remain simultaneously conscious of caste and of being a "good fellow." But I
must confess that none of it means as much to me
as the simplest muddy wooden sidewalk in Perm, or
as much as the smell of a single lime tree by the
dachas while, at four on Sundays, the German band
plays in the square.

Such visions always rise up to dog any other

imaginative versions of life I may have: wherever
I go I see babushkas with kerchiefs, high cheekbones, carp in still ponds, and doctors in steel spec-
tacles comforting rich girls to the sound of the
watchman's metallic hours; gluttons and gamblers
who fall exhausted on mounds of sturgeon, white-
fish, millet, black bread, and kvass; steppes, troikas,
carpet slippers, a *barin* spat upon by the slaves he
has freed and a multitude of unfinished projects of
self-reformation.

I am pursued by notions of the Russian character
and the Russian soul that I have picked up from a
few weeks in the choir of the Russian church that
is in the back yard of the Old St. Patrick's in New
York, or from two *paschas* on Long Island (one of
which was nearly called off because the hostess'
dog had died and was held anyway because the next
day she felt better and the dog, she said, "would
have wanted it that way") that are memorable for
my having danced with people of disproportionate
size and energy and eaten excessively of huge pies
and cakes and stuffed cabbage.

There are special Russians, too, who intrude, like
my friend Guivi (wherever you are, Guivi, may this
reach you), the son of a Georgian army doctor and
a French mother and the twin of all those splendid
Georgian and White Russian dynasties in New York
that survive only for the weddings and burials of
their kindred: a gentle madman, a Pechorin un-
horsed, a Myshkin among thieves. Guivi was exactly
the type of whom the good people of Iowa City
(where I met him) would have said, when their
own teen-agers weren't out playing Blackout or
Chicken on the long, straight, narrow roads, that
he "would come to no good end." And of course he
did not. Along West Market Street he would zoom
past midnight on his motorcycle (memories of the
French Resistance? And if so, what side was he on?)
with a beautiful, as-cultivated-as-the-finest-flower
Negro girl astride his back saddle; or into the house
he would stroll, small, dark, and mustached, cadging
food or drink or time to pass, holding a hand or

kissing one gallantly or just as much at home walking the dog. He might suggest, in the same tone as he would suggest *une partie de plaisir,* to smash up my car and, waxing enthusiastic, might describe ingenious insurances and corrupted mechanics who were part of the plan. And, indeed, he did finally carry out such a conspiracy with a car or cars that were not his by Iowa definitions, so that the next time we saw him was in the Iowa State Penitentiary in Ames. There, with his broken mystical English, he was teaching spelling to the inmates with all the joy of a Tolstoy writing out ABC's. Now we write all the people who have ever known him and receive no answer. He was deported, we know; but has France accepted him back? No forwarding address is on all the envelopes we address him. He is like that Russia that is in my mind, gone, but persistently there, clear and well-loved.

Not only people, but history haunts me, too: the Mongol yoke; the German knights dragging their casques and cloaks after them into the frozen lake; the Boyars; Ivan showered with coins; Peter laying out his theocentric city with its windows to the West and its soul to the East; Catherine's court and elegant Europeans like Ségur and Ligne on a galley watching fireworks while the Porte is humbled; the nineteenth-century czars, from Alexander and his vainglory to the last desperate Romanovs caught in the webs of all their forebears.

All of it is deeply affecting, because it is as though Russian history were the history of the entire monarchical age done up into one bright metaphor, the mores of the courts arriving late there and finding in Russia their most ferocious and unmeasured adherents, the institutions of the monarchy overwhelming, the poverty on which they were based indescribable, and the unreality of the power defying imagination and sanity. In the century of dissolution, from Napoleon to the 1917 Revolution, Russia presents a picture of such complexity and sickness that nothing is comparable to it, save perhaps the body itself in dissolution, in its last hour. This image well expresses why Russia in the nineteenth century exercises such a fascination on so many minds, for this sickness and death the Russians have lived through is the sickness and death of our civilization. The Russians survived it *for* us, and that is a debt we can never repay.

When these are the events on which our life is based, it is hard to forget Rasputin finding it convenient to be murdered several times by the flowers of the nobility, being poisoned only to seem in perfect health, then stabbed, then shot, then cast into the Neva only to be seen swimming. Port Arthur sticks with me, and so do the men packed into the long hot wood-burning trains that stopped everywhere at sidings and before gradients, to let the soldiers stew in their dreams after glory, only to reach their incredible destination and find themselves outflanked and sold out, given neither ammunition nor replacements and yet performing such heroisms as men can find to perform in a particularly brutal war. There is a sense, too, of the restless masses behind them, thousands of miles away, aware that something is very wrong, but not sure of what or why. I remember those ironclads, too, steaming around the Cape and across the Indian Ocean, hot and flat, lumbering as elephants in mud, armor clanking, boilers bursting, white-shirted and bepompomed sailors swarming in the quickstep the newsreels of those days give them: only to be blown up in one great incompetent day at Tsushima, magazines strewn over the entire Japan Sea and the mouths of the crew slowly filled with oil slick and hissing steam.

For that matter there are the eight million men or four million (there being little difference between the two figures) who were churned up in Galicia or along the Baltic in mud or mad misery: one doubts if the unknown four million can have meant much even to one of *them* that can have expected little else when, snatched off the hayricks at harvest, marched off at forced drafts, they were finally delivered shoeless, weaponless, officerless, and thoughtless to several obscure winters and fly-infested summers between 1914 and 1917, only to be promptly sold out at Brest-Litovsk. And that token force with its silly grins plastered along the rails of a transport in Marseilles (many miles through the Bosporus and Aegean), taken up to Paris to be feted (who had come, their country's finest, to express solidarity between the mud of Galicia and the mud of the Somme), and then proving refractory and having to be shipped off into camps where their disaffection could fester into open rebellion at Courteline. Who can eradicate the Romanovs, all those grand-dukes and grand-duchesses, mere beautiful children and wards of the twentieth century, from an elastic conscience? I see them always working in their vegetable garden, the Czarina in a wheel chair with needlework in her hands and the rest of them in white naval uniforms, or, God save us when it is a matter of children, in sailor suits: not at all indignant, the photographs show, but bowing before some superior force. Meanwhile, back in St. Petersburg . . . there is the Duma and those gentlemen in frock coats during the brief months of parliamentary Anglomania, that absurd interregnum of the tattersall waistcoat and the country squire and the honorable member (with something not quite in keeping, for instead of the clipped mustache there is the ostentatious forestry of the Russian beard in the midst of which the lips are like gleaming waves on a lolling ocean). What a body that was, Ukrainians fractured, liberals split, radicals intransigent, the go-slows against the go-fasts, and Comrade Lenin puffing into the Finland Station, taking a few cursory looks to tot up their incompetences, to see these gentlemen scurrying about their memorials and memoranda, then sending them packing with a good old-fashioned lockout. "What's Kornilov to you?" I ask myself, "and Kolchak? And the Czech Legion? Siberia? Escapes to Finland, armored trains, the hoods in the woods, the thugs in the suburbs, the boys shot, the women raped, estates burned, wealth destroyed and raw, human horror, hunger and hatred and sorrow and sacrifice?"

The answer is, that it is very much indeed, that modern history knows nothing like it unless it is the catastrophic attempt to destroy the Diaspora. It has more reality for me than any other part of history. It is so easy to understand why it happened.

Images, people, history—all these transformations that the imagination creates from reality continued once inside the Coliseum. I became bewitched all over again. The escalator was miraculously altered into that steam-bound third-class carriage where Myshkin and Rogozhin met on their way from Warsaw to Petersburg; it became, as the railroads were for Dostoevsky, the iron choker of Western Civilization, the rattling tracks of the Apocalypse; that train that crushed Anna's body while leaving her soul intact; or nearly a century later, the line onto which looked the camps of the German generals penned in captivity on their journeys home. The railroads of Russia are not just railroads: everyone knows that the rolling stock of the West cannot move there.

When the escalator was done with me, I found myself in a vast hangar, where the size of everything suggested further: the journey to the Far East, for instance, which is seven days with a samovar in every car; which during the Civil War took two months to get no further than Tomsk, humanity clinging to the wooden sides like so many flies and only the commissars sitting stolid and unrelenting in empty compartments; a journey which, when Katusha and Prince Nekhlyudov made it, among the leg-irons and shaven heads, across cold fords and bitter ferries, would have thought two months no more than a day.

But time seemed to have betrayed me, too, for surely this gigantic worker I saw leaning on a sardine key, this huge snail-shell with its digestive tract of Russian science, these massy cars and huge nuclei are not the same Russia I have described. The reality is machines and all the rest, my flights of fancy, was compounded of dreams, travels in Gogol's troika, whence it is now time to step down, for this is the end of the line, and consider modern Russia, which is machines, machines, all of them looking vaguely dangerous: the mute machines with their glassy eyes and itchy switches, the glassy-eyed visitors watching as it were, the very machines mate and multiply, looking about longingly for something familiar or something human; didn't Mr. Khrushchev say it in San Francisco? "When we were about to launch our first rocket . . . the scientists invited us members of the government to see the rocket. Well, we went and looked at it. We looked at it from this side, from that side, we looked down upon it, we looked up at it. We thought it was all very interesting indeed. But what the thing was, none of us knew."

If this is the new age, and Russia has it, then I expected the kids to be fascinated. After all, it's going to be their bloody world, not mine. I am safe in my regal dreams in which Jules Munshin wears a white silk shirt and speaks outrageous Archdukese. But fortunately, the kids were just kids, which means there is hope for the world still. They watched the model of the atomic icebreaker *Lenin* because its insides were all lit up like an electric whale and the airfield because the planes came in on guy-wires in a blaze of red and green lights. And how they clustered about the TV camera to be caught by its eye and appear on the screen, baring their teeth, thumbing their noses, plastering down their hair, popping their bubble gum: God bless them all!

There are many who think that in this plethora of material goods, it is only a matter of time until the American spiritual malaise catches up to Russia. But it was precisely the Russian attempt *not* to let this happen that struck me most about the Exhibition; for the Russians did not display only machines or only their version of the classless life, they were also trying to show that material strength could be spiritualized through constantly reaffirming the ideal rather than the real condition of Russian life and

thus binding each citizen forever, and through conviction, to the common patriotic tasks implied in
making the ideal real.

Which means that Russia does not change, no more
than the rest of us do. What these machines make,
what they *do*, is easy enough to understand, and *how*
they do it will always be of concern to some; but
the imagination itself is outstripped by so much invention and our capacity to absorb so much of this
New Age is diminished. Nuns will fly to the moon
primping their coifs; the circuits will think, store,
and answer. But meanwhile the family car will
break down and toasters will burn out. The machines
may multiply, but they, too, die from their exertions.
They make errors and the giants among them thud
wearily and stop; lights flicker and grow dim. The
heavenly mathematics falters. Thinking the way I
do, or the way you do, is still absolutely unique; living as I do or as you do is still my concern, or yours:
what is important, then, is what we think and how
we live.

II

You have to be a lot older than I am to remember
Fourth of July parades when they meant something.
There was a time when in the hot small squares
well-scrubbed boys gulped down their speeches, a disproportionate majority of trombones blared and
thin-legged majorettes made young pimples rise;
school principals wore flowing locks and black
velvet ties and past winners of county oratorical
contests regaled crowds with "our great nation";
and I do believe there was gladsomeness and festiv-
ity and thankfulness to hear those words and to be
an American. It was hot, the chestnut trees sagged
just as they do now, the speakers spoke certainly
not more briefly: but the words, then, were fresh
and had meaning. To each listener those words
"greatness," "freedom" meant something personal
and tangible. Those words and all the rest of the
oratory made each listener's pride in his country
legitimate.

And I suspect that in Russia today, on some white and dusty road between rows of beeches, or even in some oil-soaked and smoky plant with its acres and acres of whining, warming, golden machinery, the words, the gestures, the songs, the banners, the old-time types, the jingo and the slogan, still have their meaning; as each listener has his pride.

At some point patriotism had this meaning for me; and then I got educated out of it. I wish someone had refrained from telling me it was childish. It happened at some point in my first year at boarding school. I remember praying that we would get into the war, just so that something, *anything*, might happen. We did, and learned to disassemble jeeps and reassemble fractures rather more than we learned Cicero; and then, suddenly, patriots in the flesh were a bit too much. I can recall the first instance, when our confessor, a stubborn, fat, frazzle-haired Irish priest with an automatic rigmarole in the hot little box ("Sins of Impurity? How many? Do you really want to stop? Five Hail Marys."), who knew no other kind of sin or of any contrition, altered his custom to become a patriot. I can recall how out of place suddenly seemed, in my earnest resolutions of self-improvement, the formula he added then, when we were in the war, just before absolution, "Let us pray for our country and its brave soldiers."

I wish the good father had not said this and others hadn't talked me out of waving my flag. Not that I approve of patriotism, but because it seems to me something that one must grow out of, or transcend, oneself, and not to wind up with world-weariness and cynicism. It's a question, isn't it, whether, when we are all the same, we shall be any better? When our bloods are inter-muddied and our races intermingled and our beliefs interchangeable, shall we cease to conceive of ways to make ourselves distinct one from the other?

Actually, this is all taken care of for us by the human rat-race in which we live: he whose threshold of vision is at the level of "one more deal" has no time to consider what he is, his generic tag, his inheritance; even had he time, it is not chic or cool for him to think beyond his itchy palm. The best and the worst of such thoughts, of our country or our culture, have become inextricably mixed, and our distaste for the worst of these, for rapine, jingo, bluster, folly, oppression, war, "heroic" charges, lost causes, and popinjays, has obscured the best that may reside in many of the same things, our self-image, our self-revelation, our communality, our tenderness. The negative and the positive are so confused that we cannot distinguish between the joy of being what we are and the miserable fear that makes us despise those who are not what we are: rather than be the latter, we eschew the former altogether.

And meanwhile, around the land, the professional patriots take our places, politicos and toastmasters, the ancien regime and the women. Wherever you go you will find the last. On rickety or well-polished platforms, stately behind glasses, vitreous behind jugs of iced water, pink behind high ruffled collars of cascading cottons, there stands an army of matrons; in committee and in charity they take possession of what men have abandoned, but that men must still live or die with and women merely fatten and batten on.

I have an aunt by marriage of whom I could not be fonder; she is lovely and kind, wears red shoes on her tiny feet whether at weddings or funerals, and has an abundance of love for her family and home: yet not a month goes by that her familiar picture is not in the newspapers with a rubric underneath stating how she is heading a committee, forming part of one or being one, to fight tyranny, subversion, the peril from within, the peril from without. I say, this is a woman who dances at her daughters' weddings not wrapped in the flag but in tiny red shoes. The business of her life fills me with a kind of pathos, for it is unreal that she should be so concerned; any man who has been at or near war knows that war has nothing to do with ideals,

with anti-fascism or anti-communism. War *is;* it is
one of the worst aspects of that sort of patriotism
she preaches.

III

What, then, is patriotism? And is there a just
kind? It is the feeling of intimacy an individual has
with his society; it is a reflection of his concern for,
his pride in, his commitment to the things he identifies with the particular genius of his land. It is a
matter of faith; an *article* of faith. It cannot be
challenged in any usual way, with argument or per-
suasion, fashion or currency.

Now, when you look at Russia, there are some
extraordinary arguments bound up in this article of
faith. Take that which Dostoevsky advances in
The Idiot: "Don't try to frighten me with your
prosperity, your wealth, the infrequency of famine
and the rapidity of the means of communication.
There is more wealth, but there is less strength.
There is no uniting idea; everything has grown
softer, everything is limp and everyone is limp."
This is nothing more than God-seeking radicalism,
seeking past temporary benefits, and the emphasis
on the *unifying idea* is an unvarying emphasis in
Russia; if the Soviet state is described by Americans
as a monolith, it is not without cause. To Danilevsky,
for instance, the forces of darkness are synonymous
with middle-class Western society, "with its spirit
of greed embodied in capitalism and its violent
internal dissensions . . . its racial and class strife."
Khomyakov carries the argument even further; he
is even more subtly intransigent on the matter of
individualism: "Each human being finds himself
within the Church, not in the impotence of spiritual
isolation, but in the strength of spiritual oneness with
his brethren and his Saviour . . ." and for Khomyakov's "Church" and "Saviour" here we can read
"country" and "leader." "The isolated individual,"
he goes on to say, "is marked by complete impotence
and irreconcilable discord": he acquires strength
only by living in a morally healthful relationship to

the social whole. Khomyakov even goes so far as to say that "the truth is inaccessible to individual thinkers . . . it is accessible only to an aggregate of thinkers, bound together by love."

Well, part of this preoccupation with unity and inner harmony is that tendency of the Slav world in general to seek the whole man, a notion they inherited from Greece through Byzantium. But beyond this, here is also a solid opposition to the pettifogging of the West, an attempt to tumble down the whole rational structure of the separateness of powers within an individual or a state. The Slav cannot say, "He is an excellent Secretary of Justice, but as a human being he is a failure"; one part cannot be separated from the other. In fact, there is a strong feeling that there cannot *be* such a thing as human failure: all is redeemable, even as the Orthodox Church clings intuitively to the belief in universal salvation.

The whole man or nothing; the whole state or nothing. There is a Scythian element in Russian thinking, an open-eyed acceptance of the possibility of an apocalypse. There is also an impatience with gradualism: the Duma crumbled on this and Tolstoy, after all, demanded nothing less than perfection of himself. The West has not carried things to their extremes: it may cost us our civilization. The 1917 Revolution announced Tabula Rasa; it abandoned all the rules. It is one of the most admirable and horrifying of all historical events, for never was a nation so purged of all its codes, of all its internal logic, so sharply, so suddenly, so drastically, and at the same time never was a purge accomplished in a way more contradictory to the nature of Western man—including that prime rule of Western man which says that nothing succeeds but that which sees beyond the hour, that which has the force of rational logic and profit (not merely economic, but social) with it.

In the eyes of Russia, we ourselves stand condemned. "The logic of history is passing sentence on the spiritual life of Western Europe," says Khomyakov. The reason? Rationalism, which Khomyakov calls "logical knowledge isolated from the moral principle," our concern with self-interest: the very reason with which we condemn 1917 and the times since.

It is no accident that the Slavophiles—and these include, to varying degrees, all the rulers Russia has had for a century—besides calling Moscow the Third Rome, the logical heir to Byzantium, also thought of Russia as the Second Israel: "This people," says Danilevsky as he makes the identification, "is justly called 'The people chosen by God.'" The messianic function of a society permeates Russian history. In religious terms first, and now in partly secular terms (for one should not under- emphasize the religious force of the Soviet state), Russia has followed the Hassidic dictum that all things may and must be hallowed. The Russians have applied it to history and political action: all action must be holy. In the nineteenth century the state was openly identified with religion in Ouva- rov's famous formula, *Samoderyavie, Pravoslavie, Narodnost:* Autocracy, Orthodoxy, and Nationality; and Gogol openly called Russian culture "Orthodox Culture."

Unity, community, messianism: these are as in- extricably fixed in my memories of the Exhibition as they are in my understanding of nineteenth- century Russia. In some mysterious way both camps at the Exhibition, the Russians who had created it and the Americans who were observing it, lay under a spell of religiosity. I don't mean priests, evangel- ists, cranks, and pissprophets (though there were plenty there), nor the reckless-haired Irishman who went about among the machines mumbling, mis- takenly, "They just don't believe in God." Such people are committed to a formal notion of religion, one that is tangible or it does not exist. I am speak- ing of the plain fervor the Exhibition expressed and aroused in many.

I know that officially we of the "Western World" are all skeptics. That battle was fought long ago and darkness and God lost. Skepticism is the yo-yo, the beanie, the Davy Crockett of the moment, a parlor game for progressive suburbanites and any fool, as though a relative world precluded judgment. But consider for how many at that Exhibition skepticism was an inverse form of faith. Consider how many were skeptical because they wished to hang on to some myth pap-fed into them, that the Soviet Union was one great concentration camp of starved and enslaved peoples awaiting liberation, or were skeptical because the material plenty exposed was not packaged in the familiar red-white-and-blue wrappings of freedom, plenty, and democracy. In such circumstances skepticism is not a rational process; it is the result of a mass dazzlement. Some hoped that Russia would be destroyed; a handful, that she would redeem the world. Some feared to hope; some shut their eyes. Fear and hope: they alternate in our national attitudes. But somehow it is very wrong to fear more than one hopes. The kind of fear under which the fearful live, of the yellow peril, the Tartar hordes, Godless communism, destroys life itself: it is preventive fear, prophylactic fear.

But I have observed, in those societies over which the wings of greatness are passing, as an invisible hand, always, a religious fervor. There is no greatness without it, even if, as in the Encyclopedists' age, it was the fervor of reason. It can seem absurd sometimes in the mouths of its ministers, as it did in the mouth of a French plenipotentiary I recently heard, who compared De Gaulle to Joan of Arc, saying that where Joan "had saved France only once, De Gaulle had saved her twice." On his lips it sounded tasteless and vulgar; but in many mouths it has the odor of sanctity and the supernatural seems near. Churchill possessed it, and England, during the war; Haiti with Toussaint; and we ourselves in and with Lincoln. But these are momentary manifestations, "morning mushrooms" Jeremy Taylor would call them: still, they catch our aspirations and they leave a rich taste on the palate. They are words and not words, as the Mass is. A man who speaks these words of grandeur is soon revealed as a fool or a cheat if he does not believe them, for the real ones do not possess vision, they are possessed by vision. The humblest act of their lives witnesses to the vision and they are disconcerting when set loose among the slothful of soul. Though often it is carried too far, to lying, stealing, and killing, its mark is that it makes diverse men brothers, not in the pursuit of something profitable to each, but in the pursuit of something for which they may be expected to sacrifice everything they possess. It is a kind of patriotism I would not mind possessing. But "there is no uniting idea; everything has grown softer, everything is limp and everyone is limp."

IV

But let us consider, momentarily, that we do have a unifying idea, and that this idea is freedom: for after all, when we wish to condemn those who are not ourselves, we say "not of the free world."

We are free, to be sure—not to visit China, nor to agitate among the masses or write with absolute impunity or, on the other side, to despise Negroes or Jews, refuse taxes or oppose war; still, we know what the word means. Within the world that we acknowledge as our own, within the margin of error and eccentricity allotted to us, we may do as we please; given an income and the *independence* that money provides in a capitalist society and the tolerance of a mass of heterodox opinions about us, we may get away with much. We are not spoken for by De Gaulle's Sureté men, ready with electric wires for our genitals; we do not live in fear, though we often fear we will. Nor do we live entirely un-protected against the superior malice of the State, and our society is not yet lacking in those who will defend their own rights through ours. But are we free? And what is freedom?

For instance, we take it for granted that we are free, because we say we are free; we have repeated the word often enough for us to be enslaved by it. We conceive of this freedom as having special prop-

erties all its own, quite apart from the benefits it
sheds on all of us; it is magic. But our freedom is
only worth the exercise of it; it is no better than the
use we put it to.

We are free to protest, and the question is, What
should we protest? And how? By my nature I am
drawn to those who wish to put an end to nuclear
testing, to ban atomic warfare, but I have never been
able to join up with a single committee, because I
have never found one that would protest on what I
consider the right grounds, which are, not that one
should oppose the bomb because we may all be destroyed, but because *any single person* may be hurt.
The argument is simple: What right has anyone, in
any way, to take the life or the health of any individual? I find we are free to protest, but that in our
very freedom lies the danger: that we shall not see,
because protest, limited protest, is made easy for
us, and comparatively harmless, that our freedom
must be exercised on the highest grounds and with
no instant of compromise.

Yet one of the things we value most about our
freedom is the political structure it has brought upon
us, the democratic society. In ours, the issues are
not posed to us, and hence our protests become
individual protests and as so many puffs of smoke.
I would swear that a majority of my countrymen
would favor a prohibition on atomic warfare, but it
is a referendum that will never be taken. Democracy,
this creature of our freedom, is a fallible instrument
in any age in which the ideas involved in choosing are
not more powerful than the two or more concrete
alternatives offered. Freedom was not a weapon
forged for automatic societies spiraling into com-
plexities that lie far beyond choice.

But if we return to the common-sense notion of
being "free," by which we understand that we are
unhampered to varying degrees in varying places
and at varying times by constraints of whatsoever
sort, we must realize that we are indeed free. The
chief question then remaining is, Is it worthwhile to
be free? We shall have to ask ourselves whether

freedom really corresponds to the power and the
majesty with which we have invested that word,
whether it offers the healing balm to our daily
wounds that the magic implies. I feel that it does not,
because I think we have lost our reasons for being
free. We have our freedom but we do not make it
serve any useful purpose and so it rots in our souls
and becomes personal irresponsibility; it is a nox-
ious, corrupting vapor that smells of the rankest
egotism. Our freedom—and I mean as much our
"national" freedom as our personal freedom—is
alienated from the moral intent and the ethical
connotations it once possessed. For where once we
wished to be free to enjoy to the fullest the *Civitas*,
to implement our aspirations, to make something of
ourselves and our corporate selves, we now take
freedom to mean something infinitely more common-
sense, the absence of constraints.

It is here that Russian history has come to mean
so much to me, and not merely Russian history, but
that sense of unity and purpose that is particularly
theirs. For where we often invest our private lives
with moral earnestness, and I know of no people more
concerned intellectually with the right and wrong
of individual human acts, the Russian invests and
has invested both his private and his social lives
with that same earnestness and he has been im-
measurably the richer for it, both as an individual
and as a member of society. In our more selfish concerns, with our Western anthropocentrism, we have
become insecure and increasingly uncertain of our
power, as human beings or as a nation, and we who
were once the moral image of the world are now
barely sufficient as a moral image to ourselves.

This social earnestness does not necessarily indicate any superiority in its visible results: the prod-
ucts of such national attitudes are not in question
and many of the world's mishaps are due to mis-
placed zeal of this kind; indeed, many of Russia's
mishaps. It is the quality that I consider important.

Freedom without this quality is not worth much;
it is not even *living* much, though on the surface it

would seem that the "free" man lives more. But take the Army, for instance, and the war, which was the central experience of my generation. Why is it only that that stirs all of us in our thirties and forties to something that we all acknowledge belongs to each of us and yet to all? Each of us has almost total recall of every incident, while the years before and since are often submerged in a blur. This is the one event that made us all one. Resentment we may have felt, hatred even, anger, pain, anguish, but reality was never so much with us, except perhaps in those other transcending experiences that are common to all of us, love, death, family, home. A sense of isolation may be delicious; it can be cultivated and most appreciated when it is hard to obtain. But generally it is a burden, for all that it is praised. We are not lonely and useless because we like being lonely and useless, but because by and large each of us spends his life trying to be what he is not: an individual, alone, strong, self-sufficient, ambitious, and as avaricious of joy as he is clandestine about pain.

V

"Useless." I wrote the word myself, about myself. But I know that I am not alone. Many of us feel useless. That is to say, we do not feel "used"; we are spending our lives short of our optimum. I've sat around New York apartments like the next man and listened to bright young men who, playing Guggenheim, glutted with French films and Italian opera and bridge once a week, tell me that Albert Schweitzer is the world's greatest bore: and so are all people who take up the salvation or the *misericordia* of others. In their rabbit hutches, human ants on top floors and all the floors in between, coddled by the kindness of the incomes they earn providing nothing of use to the world, this idle conversation serves to round out their own boredom. I don't worship Schweitzer; in fact with a kind of snobbism that horrifies me, I tend to reject my heroes the moment everyone else takes them up, but surely there is

more in what *he* does than in what *they* do: or are
all our values somehow changed?

I remember well, being nineteen—and often since,
but not in the same places or the same circumstances,
or even alas, with the same fervor—sitting in the
eyrie on Mott Street before I got married. It seemed
to us then that the life we were leading was essentially not much of a life. The city seemed stale to
us; or we were stale, too stale for it. I think great
cities, like loves, have to be rediscovered periodically.
We were stale on the art shows, the concerts, the
writers, with all that dazzled our eye or beguiled
our time, all the things that are seductions from the
inner life. The apartment was warm and steamy and
over the ice-box was a shelf with several hundred
Pepsi bottles, that were our accumulation against
rainy days. We thought that we would go West when
we were married; we would do something useful
with the little knowledge that we had. The wildest
place, it seemed to us, must be the Dakotas: they
suggested sod houses, mile-sections, and snowfilled
skies. Neither of us imagined the motels or highways
or banks. We would teach there because we were not
trained enough to fight the tsetse fly, because we
were not holy enough to convert the savages, not
heroic enough to tackle the poorest, too shy to take
on the criminal, not sure enough of ourselves to comfort the sick or the mad or the deformed. It was service and action that moved us and we were warmed by
our own generosity (this is not always a false emotion) and perhaps by a suspicion that we would never
do what we said we would do because we would feel
faintly ridiculous doing so, and would not know how
to begin: charity is so organized; our skills were so
few. And now, a decade later, though the Pepsi
bottles are still not turned in regularly nor without
excitement, Mott Street has given way to a house
and a garden, servants and responsibilities. But the
urge is still with us, ineradicable, causing guilt and
pain, stepping cruelly on our inadequacies, making
us aware (oh, at irregular intervals) of the prompt-
ings of conscience, which says, "Do something,

gives. . . ." Year by year it becomes harder to give.
Months go by and we do not even hear of *someone*
who is giving, or doing. We listen to the rationaliza-
tions that our world offers us: "Be yourself, be a
man in the fullest sense, develop what is within you
and giving will radiate from within you." And
whenever we think of Russia, other alternatives
suggest themselves and it seems to us that we would
willingly sacrifice ourselves to the creation of some
new civilization; and equally, we are aware that this
is all fantasy and that we would not there, either.

For that, life in Russia, is a gray life, so we are
told by those who have been; and when you escape
from it, you feel a real freedom, as though you have
escaped from a damp prison. But our life in America
is of such a profound selfishness that the word
"gray" loses its meaning. What sort of madness is
it that allows *Vogue*'s language—"an adorable, puck-
ish bra, tight as Maytime"—in the same world as
Dolci's report on Sicily, in a world where Arabs live
in sordid tin shacks and Indians rot on raw rice,
where Africans are shot and clubbed for exercising
their rights not to be animals, and where, in our own
country, our fellow citizens cannot eat, sleep, live, or
learn next to their countrymen? *The New Yorker*,
our civilization's summum of chic, the distillation of
all the suave horrors of snobbishness, can advertise
the fabulous swimming pool of the Bulova Estate,
air-conditioned, climatized, lucite-covered, and I
suppose it would be a gray life indeed if the estate
were used to take some Puerto Rican family out of
its six-in-a-room slum or to provide some decent
place for the poor to die as though someone cared:
that *would* make life gray. So the asking price is
575,000 dollars and no doubt some popcorn prince
or thick-knotted cravat of a popular singer will up
and buy it. If we are to be free to spend and buy and
this is the best we can offer, I suppose we must be
urged to do just that and that that is better than
some tithe to education or social action. And those
gray Russians, *U.S. News & World Report* tells
us with supreme confidence, want exactly what we

want, they complain of the grayness of the life they lead. And if this is so, it is a shame that no society has ever survived which thought beyond its own comforts to the agonies of others. And I say that without this ardor, without this desire to exceed oneself, it is hard to get through life and harder yet to bring it to a proper end, and that is all that counts.

Are *Vogue*'s bra and the Bulova Estate all we have to offer? Is this what our freedom amounts to? We are so *afraid* of being regimented, even for our own good; yet, though we look down on joiners, we do join. We join comfort; we join wealth; we join pleasure and leisure. Our slavery is simply more subtle than the gray Russian variety and more comfortable; it is subtly economic. It is to live that we work; to enjoy that we pay; to consume that we enjoy. On the first of the month we unite with our fellow men in the glorious task of paying the installments and the bills, paying for our status and our desires, both true and pretended. Is there any greater regimentation than the need for money? Money is ingrained in us, and if it did not exist, we would invent it.

The Russians have an ingenious variation on this regimentation we fear: they regiment by choice. Not by free choice in the sense we mean free, but by offering the choice between uselessness and isolation and living in a moral Coventry and that of utility, pride, and community. On this point alone, the intricacy of the links between nineteenth-century Russia and Soviet Russia is wonderfully interesting. That same Khomyakov a century ago argued thus about the role of individual freedom in regard to the Church: "Forced unity, in matters of faith, is a lie . . . and forced obedience is death." The individual is then free in matters of faith? Not at all: "This freedom serves in no sense as an individualizing function. Freedom belongs to the Church *as a whole*. . . . Although the believer's freedom is not subject to any external authority, it is justified by his oneness of thought with the Church." No more subtle argument for the loss of *some* freedom, for *some* gain, was ever advanced. And this argument is as central to the Soviet state as it was to the Orthodox state the Slavophiles envisioned.

Of course one can rebel against the poverty of taste that this choice between community and isolation often entails, against the thick-headed and thick-ankled bureaucracy of the approach to life through discomfort, against boredom and mediocrity, against Puritanism and the excessive enforced togetherness of Russian life; but there is a power that subtends all the ugliness and transcends all the defects that machinery creates, and that is the power that any individual feels in the exercise of justice and virtue, in having his resources tapped, *ad majorem Dei Gloriam*, regardless of the god. Our society does not offer us this power. Instead, it offers us pain and shame in a hundred ways.

For I feel sick and foolish, small and ridiculous, to think that the best we can offer in the exercise of our democracy is a cross-purposed, cross-tempered, inarticulate man as President; that our ideals consist of a balanced budget and a clean bomb, the filthy version of which we alone have used in war; that our leaders are all sick, with cancer, the heart, the joints, or the mind. I am ashamed of the penalties of prosperity, the toll taken by our selfishness in spite of the world's ills and needs, of the absence of just causes. After all, we have been spared: most of the destructions of the last wars have fallen on others; others have been persecuted, or starved, or oppressed. It is hard to reckon what our isolation from tangible suffering has cost us. The graves of those that died in the war are not for the most part on our soil; they have not the immediacy that that tablet on the wall does in Paris that says here, in this spot where you walk by, fell a seventeen-year-old, fresh from the Lycée, caught beyond his capacities in the deadliest of games, or of that railroad depot that stands a ruin where once you left on a honeymoon in a white hat: these things are holy to your memory and they are present throughout life, while we bear few visible scars.

There is a Byzantine unreality about our lives in the face of the events of the twentieth century that must have struck Khrushchev particularly during his visit in Hollywood to *Can-Can,* which apparently was the most we could offer him. And somewhere behind the irresponsibility of our pleasure lies the holocaust of history, ready to engulf us. We glory in the individual, but we have made no provision for the sheer luxuriousness of this notion. And the Russians, and behind them the Chinese (as an exquisitely literate "expert" put it in Chicago recently, "by the turn of the century *slightly more than every other person* will be a Chinese"), are slowly laying down the bases of the civilizations of the future, those amorphous, hierarchized, rigid, and stable structures wherein the individual as we now know him will have no viable existence save in self-perfection and voluntary participation in the progress of his society.

VI

The world today preys on our fears; it makes distinctions and says I may be a Russophile, but may not love *this* Russia, because this Russia has done thus and so and intends furthermore and elsewhat. The disillusioned true-believers stand watch on the portals of sympathy; the ex-communists turn the signposts about and make a maze of a straight path; and the experts and junketers come and go to and from the seat of revelation bearing unscathed with them the vessels of their original preconceptions. In all of these, some hardening of the arteries of conversion has taken place; the worst of them (and these must also be the worst Russians) urge us to "change before it is too late," to "catch up" or "surpass": it is as though the individual precious parts of a way of life were as interchangeable as the parts of a Ford.

I loathe this fear they seek to instill in me. Fear as a state of mind is something a man consents to:

once he is afraid, he fears to lose his fear, for every
time he consents to being afraid, another barrier
goes up between himself and the object of his fear
until ultimately the structure is so much larger than
his soul that he can never break out.

Why should I be frightened of what was before
my time, or that is part of another man's ken and
not my own? Every man learns for himself and
seeks the truth with the evidence of his own heart,
and if men learned anything from generation to
generation, this would be the Millennium. I loathe
this fear; I dislike being told what the proper objects
of my anger are. I can find my own. Koestler and
Malraux, Plivier and Orwell, I am speaking to you:
the crimes you describe are terrible, but what are
they to me? A richer sense of the present, but not
something I can act by. History is not fated; act does
not follow act in any prescribed pattern. Besides,
the problems are not so simple.

I was in Berlin just after the War when the rapes
of the Soviet Occupation were still fresh in the minds
of the population. But alas! I had come there from
the French Zone, in which the Berber troops had
been loosed; and the *Fraüleins* we enjoyed were not
so enjoyed out of mere camaraderie. The poor Ger-
mans were the victims in every case; but were they
innocent? And so on, backwards, up the chain of
responsibility, to where it seems there is no end to
man's guilt until one realizes that, thank God, there
is no end either to his virtue.

Faith and hope are precious possessions. What I
know or feel about Russia leads me to share their
faith and their hope—for themselves. Faith is not
something a man consents to; nor is it something
he discovers through reason. It is either central to a
man or it is not; it has only a vestigial relationship
to the mind, and even that relationship is precarious
as that between two people who though they do not
love each other, see no real object in living altogether apart. Hope, too, is an overriding emotion. It
is not mere expectation, but a gladness, a clapping of
the hands, a vision of the future. These are the im-

pressions I bore away from the Exhibition. They confirm all that I know.

So that, if this contest of ideologies is so central, if it is the major issue of our time; if it is impossible to be a Russophile and still be part of the Western world; then I would like, for myself, to fight that war on the plane of faith and ideas. I would as soon see the future with faith and hope and do my share in bringing it about as betray myself and all civilization by being oblivious of that future and irresponsible as regards my part in it. It is enough true, as Yeats said, that "the best lack all conviction, while the worst are full of a passionate intensity." If we do not make whole what is now put asunder, then I fear the Osrics of this world with their feathers and plumes and *Vogues,* or the machines with their clanking hearts and faithless, visionless absolutism, will have the world all to themselves.

His Uncle Henry Levy
at His Coalyards

The skies will soon have emptied, and my trucks
unspool the hissing miles behind them, miles
adhesive taped on snow. My whole life luck's
been fickle; knock on wood—Elohim smiles
on them who wait for Him to do their will.
Smile, Lord. Thy curling rainbow cracks the clouds
and the fleecy sun too, causing them spill
their insides on earth's many raveled aisles
of thoroughfare, like canvasing that shrouds
furniture of such rare
material it rivals air.
And let luck come next year and years
that follow. Weatherman, how come the blades
of winter were as dull as garden shears

last year? I always bicker with last year.
And when the river flattens, and the winds
go creaking through the vacant trees and clear
some of the snow aside, I pray: for God rescinds
His cold spells even as my balance drifts
from black to red. I pray, and night and day

the gasworks' yapping hammers and five shifts
of workers chase my coal trucks to the ends
of all my streets, laying the pipes that pay
their paltry wages. Oh
a coalman has nowhere to go;
for even when, outdistancing
all needs, I'm filling half-full bins, delay
sets in and cocks an empty head for spring.

Once winter was a dragon, and revered.
Then we were young, and some of us were poor.
Its carborundum heels, like razors, sheared
inches off the old men for miles, and tore
the skin like Bible paper from my lips.
Who slayed the dragon? Papa's coal carts' wheels
or iron sliced it into mush and chips
of water. Soft coal killed it, for the poor,
who burned coal, breathed and vomited slick eels
of blackness. Only coal,
our black gold, spares the pitch-black mole
to scotch a dragon. Even God
has softened winter till my business kneels
before the cradling gas pipes in His sod.

But snow keeps falling, and the small, wet match
of sunlight wears its head off on the bright
snow's purple steel. My rusting trucks can catch
their death of cold, the shiny season might
blind them past endeavor—but their chains dig
out scales and dirty feathers of snow, sparks
and steel slivers, and my black drivers rig
the conveyors over the deep trailers till night
unhitches them, and the white foreman parks
the tractor cabs. I'll burn
my coalyards to their primal fern
before they'll waste to snow and Christ.
Dark are God's ways; but every morning larks
fire the lumped blackness He has iced.

LOVE

Have you ever been so much in love that it hurt? I have. I am. I used to think that something like this happened only in Billie Holiday records. You know, hurtin' music. But, true fact: it's real.

Now this is not just some four A.M., bar-closed funky stuff I'm putting down. It still hurts too much to play games with.

But wait—I've got a story to tell too. You see, basically I'm a writer. Short stories, a novel in progress. A few poems. A writer. I always wanted to be a writer, finally. After the clown, fireman, motorcycle policeman, lawyer, brain surgeon, boxer, matador stages had passed, I knew that I must write. So one day I quit my job as Publicity Director for the Cosmococcic Publishing Co., Inc. It was well-thought-of and good-paying ($145 per) for someone so young (24), and, as people do, everyone thought I was very, very, very foolish. I knocked off four short stories and five or six poems in four months and nobody would buy a one. Yet. And all this while I've got the most wonderfully excruciating love-monkey on my back. And I am married.

I met her more than a year ago. . . . No, that's not the place to start.

She works for a company that was going to publish an anthology I'd compiled, but then, as publishers do, decided not to. . . . No, this is too negative.

I don't know where to start. . . . Is she pretty? No. Cute? Thank God, no. Handsome? There's the word. Handsome. Beautiful. Strong high cheekbones, strong firm jawbones, Brando-Presley nose with slight rise on the end. Brown-blonde hair pulled back after starting somehow low on the sides of her smooth forehead. Skin? Fine, healthy, filled with vitamin D. And her body in a bathing suit is as wonderfully full-blown as it is elegantly neat in a dress. Or in tights.

Well, anyway, we went to Puerto Rico together for a weekend. My wife and another chap went too. But really we went for each other: me for sheer, unmitigated love, she out of curiosity. Also, we both like the sun.

We came back brown and pretty, me more in love and she kind of mixed up. You see, she has a sort of a boy friend. But not really, because he's in a deep analysis. Can't or won't do *anything* until he's graduated. I've never met him, but I've heard about him: we are not the same type at all.

Sometimes she calls me Lolita, just to remind me that she's a bit older than I am. It annoys the hell out of me. I don't want to be taken as a handsome plaything. (Which she says I am—the handsome part at least.)

Well, we came back from P.R. in fine shape, as I said. I then decided that she should come with me to San Francisco for a few years. By way of New Orleans (the only American city left for me to see), Mexico City, Yucatan, and Los Angeles. With a side trip to Las Vegas and Lake Tahoe. I've been

10,000 miles through all of Mexico and would like to
go there again. With her. It would mean giving up
quite a lot for both of us and she is deciding now.
I've already made up my mind and alerted my wife
that I am thinking of leaving in a while for a while.
But actually, as Durrell says, there is no choice in
the matter. It's all been arranged by another part
of ourselves, by something else.

I can raise about $1,500 cash right away, which
would take us in grand style. Then I'd work hard on
a novel (I've got many, many plots up here, and she
can pick out the good ones) and on the first $25,000
we'd travel to Greece, Sicily (I've got a strong,
strange urge to go to Sicily—must be the D. H.
Lawrence influence), Malta, and the rest of the
Mediterranean. Staying as long as we want. Wherever we want. Then we'd settle down for a few
months and I'd write us another good novel and
we'd go off to Japan, China—the Orient. Then one
day, and she would decide when, we'd find the place
in the world that we liked best (the Village? maybe
Paris) and start raising a family of the most beautiful, and beautifully well-adjusted kids ever to come
out of the womb.

I would be the happiest person in the space-age
world.

She, currently the nicest person in it, would be the
most gloriously rapturous woman alive in every
sphere.

I love her.

And if all this sounds like a fairy tale, it is only
because it is the first and only love I have ever had
and there is no world big enough to hold me. Leander
can swim his Hellespont; let someone else walk
through fire. I just want and need my woman.

Now.

an american fiesta

When Henry James returned from Europe to cast a cold and discerning eye on the American scene, he observed of Newport, our highest social mecca, that "it is the only place in America in which enjoyment is organized." That was in 1907, however, and our national progress is such that the only place I can think of today where enjoyment is *not* organized is 100th Street between First and Second Avenues in East Harlem. We common men are plagued more and more by the curse of leisure that the rich have had to bear for so long, and we, too, have discovered the blessings of organized enjoyment. The latest national pastime to be organized is jazz, and, appropriately enough, it first was successfully done at Newport, that town where Americans originally learned how to make a ritual of pleasure. The new rites in fact have been so successful that the name of Newport today (and to borrow again from Henry James, "let me not be suspected, when I speak of Newport, of meaning primarily rocks and waves . . .") is more widely known through its fame as a mecca for jazz than as a mecca for society.

Every year since it opened in 1954 the Newport Jazz Festival grew in size and gained world-wide attention—and this year it nearly collapsed beneath the weight of its own success. On the Saturday night of this summer's fiesta several thousand beer-inspired troops, mainly collegians, who were turned away when Newport's Freebody Park had been filled to its 15,000 capacity, attempted to storm the gates. It took the combined forces of the Newport police, the National Guard, and the U.S. Navy to quell the mob, and in the course of the battle 182 revelers were arrested and fifty wounded (though none seriously). The City Council voted in emergency session to close the show's remaining performances, and the Festival impresario, Louis Lorillard, darkly told the press that this meant the end of the annual rites.

But success dies hard in our land, and within a few short weeks Mr. Lorillard's death knell sounded premature. The Festival's board of directors sued the city for damages, saying that the crowd inside the park was perfectly orderly, and that it was the city's failure to control the unticketed hordes which caused the trouble. The city of Newport has a vital stake in the Festival, for the pilgrims spend about a million dollars each year during the three or four days of the program. Some notion of how influential this is in the thinking of the city leaders can be gotten from the fact that while armed forces were battling the rioters in the streets, the Governor was rushing to the scene from Providence, and bridge and ferry service was cut off to the city, the Council measure to halt the Festival passed by only a vote of 4-3. Two weeks later Mr. Lorillard was able to report that the councilmen were "taking deep second thoughts about banning the festival" and that the "Chamber of Commerce is coming out strongly for continuing it."

There were rumors that in the remote chance that the city carried through the ban, the Festival directors might camp next year in Yankee Stadium. In any case, the show would go on. It has by now, in its seventh year, taken its place in the ranks of such long-established American fiestas as the Rose Bowl, the Kentucky Derby, and Halloween, and no mere riot can kill it off.

I first tuned in on these new American rites by chance and by radio while sweating out a Sunday July afternoon in New York City in 1955, drinking beer and listening to the Monitor program. I had heard very little about the goings-on at Newport before that, but Monitor's breathless, on-the-scene announcers, who could make a handball game on Amsterdam Avenue sound like the Battle of the Bulge, convinced me that I had turned on something momentous. It was, they said, the second annual Festival, and the hostile older social set of Newport had not been able to stop it or stem the tide of incoming pilgrims. The beer-and-Bermuda-shorts atmosphere of gaiety was noted, music from performing combos was tuned in, and spot announcers chased their stars through the crowds to say a few words to the fans out in radioland when the sets were over. Attracted as I am to both jazz and fiestas, I determined to try to make it to Newport some Fourth of July weekend for the ceremonies, and have since succeeded in getting there and getting housed (a considerable feat) for the full duration of the festivals in 1957 and again last year. As a former observer of, and participant in, other American fiestas, ranging from fraternity Hell Week to the 500-mile Speedway race in Indianapolis (I didn't drive, I sold Coca-Cola), I feel qualified to speak about the fiesta aspects of this new native celebration in Newport.

When I got off the bus that takes the New York pilgrims from the train at Providence into Newport for the Festival, I was carrying a single suitcase, wearing a light blue summer suit of the type that every third male in New York has purchased for $27.50, and considered myself altogether inconspicuous. And yet, I was spotted and followed down the street by a group of children, who finally rushed up, yelled "Look at the Jazz Cat!," and ran off squealing, as if suspecting that I might chase after them wielding some instrument of the Devil such as a tenor sax.

Hostility on the part of the natives can of course be expected in any invasion, whether it be of a military or festival nature. Certain factions of the summer high society, rather than the year-round Newport "townies"—who profit from its business— have been appalled by the jazz intrusion, and tried to halt it. Ironically enough, the Festival began and was nurtured under the gilded wings of Mr. and Mrs. Louis Lorillard, since divorced but formerly leaders of Newport's younger society. Before any further comment about the intricacies of high society in Newport, however, I had better admit to my scant and largely imaginative understanding of it. My only personal brush with this particular layer of American life came during the 1957 Festival, when I was invited, along with several hundred other untitled individuals with press cards, to attend open house after the Festival's initial evening session, at Quatrel, the "cottage" of the Lorillards on fabled Bellevue Avenue, a broad and tree-lined thoroughfare where the Czar would have had his summer palace if he had ever come to America. I met the Lorillards in the receiving line, partook of the scrambled eggs and bourbon, attempted to spot the few true socialites among the crush of people like myself who were jamming the liquor line, and heard one beautiful girl with a voice like Daisy Buchanan's (full of money) pay homage to an aged Negro musician from Kid Ory's entourage who was planted like a potted palm in a chair in a corner of the hallway. Aside from the literal, accidental touching of shoulders with the rich whom I happened to brush on my way to more bourbon on this generous occasion, I have no personal connection with or insight into the life of Newport society. The Lorillards' divorce unhappily ended these democratic mixers on Festival nights, and no other Bellevue Avenue cottage owner has since dared to open his doors to the free-loaders of the press. Most of my historical data on these matters, then, is based by necessity on the revelations of Cleveland Amory, chronicler of *The Last Resorts,* and Doris Lilly, society columnist of the *New York Post.*

Miss Lilly reported last summer that Newport is "probably the last frontier left to the 400," which shows us just how far things have gone in this age of the rising masses. Little wonder that the Bellevue Avenue crowd resents the occupation of their last crumbling capital by the jazzmen and their followers every Fourth of July; it is the final affront to their lost glory. The more elaborate of the summer places are relics now, many of them open to sight-seeing sans-culottes who can afford the minor entrance fees. Still others, left vacant, are looted of chandeliers and statuary by fraternity boys and other barbarians who come by night to sack the halls of the departed Romans. The end of Bellevue Avenue closest to the main drag of the town, where the stores and public buildings stand in old New England brick-and-spire dignity, is scarred now by a neon shopping center, that ultimate symbol of the end of taste.

According to Cleveland Amory, the death of Mrs. Hamilton McKown Twombly in 1952, at the age of ninety-eight, "marked the end of Newport's era of elegance." Fortunately, Mrs. Twombly didn't live to see the opening of either the shopping center or the Jazz Festival. Had she lived two more years to complete a century, she would have seen (or heard) the saints of the new cult of jazz come marching into the socially hallowed halls of the old Newport Casino. The shock of this spectacle to the old guard socialites can be guessed by recalling the extent of one of their few former recognitions of the doings of the cruder world beyond. When Mrs. Astor once announced that she was going to hold a "Bohemian party," a surprised Newport colleague asked her whom she was going to invite. Her answer was: "Why, J. P. Morgan and Edith Wharton."

But when Louis Lorillard and his wife, Elaine, announced in 1954 that they were going to have a

Jazz Festival, they didn't mean that Wayne King or Paul Whiteman were coming to town. It was Albert Edward (Eddie) Condon who thumped the chord on his banjo to open the first annual rites of jazz at Newport. This same Mr. Condon was riding the riverboats with a group known as Peavey's Jazz Bandits not long after the days when Pierre Lorillard was building a special pier over the reefs in front of his Newport mansion in order to bring his yacht to the front door.

The incensed old guard of the socialites were able to drive these invaders from the Newport Casino, and later from Belcourt, a fifty-room cottage that Louis Lorillard bought as a home for the Festival, but these gestures were empty, anyhow, since the crowds of pilgrims quickly grew to such proportions that the only possible place for the fiesta was Free-body Park, Newport's outdoor arena. The only act of defiance remaining to the socialites was to hold rival balls and dinners on Festival nights, but this obviously had no effect on the jazzmen, whose standing and reputation is based on how they blow, rather than where they eat dinner. Even the overtures of the socialites friendly to the Festival had been lightly regarded by the jazz performers. When Louis Armstrong, one of the reigning saints, was asked by a reporter why he didn't show up for dinner with the Lorillards on the opening night of the 1957 Festival, he answered frankly: "A long time ago I stopped going to dinner before I have to work. You go, you get full of that whiskey and you sound bad, and the people who ask you to dinner are the first to complain. I gotta work."

The "rival" parties thrown by the socialites can at best only serve to prevent defection from their own ranks. Yet the pull of the fiesta is such that more and more of the Bellevue Avenue people show up in the boxes at Freebody Park each year, joining with the masses (not only in the park but also around the world; the Festival provides the most widely heard program of the Voice of America) to form a scene that can be no better described than it was, in 1957, by Murray Kempton in the *New York Post:*

> The American Jazz Festival opened last night for Karachi, Beirut, and Prague, and the rich people who come with their cocktail shakers to drink in the twilight while waiting for old men from New Iberia named Robichaud and Slow Drag.

What draws them all is certainly more than the Newport setting, for just as the success of the Rose Bowl spawned the Sugar, Orange, and Cotton bowls, the Newport event set off the chain reaction of the Playboy, the Monterey, the Boston, and a rash of other jazz festivals. According to *Billboard* magazine, last year's was the longest outdoor jazz season on record, beginning May 29 on a Hudson River passenger boat and ending in October with the festival at Monterey. Fourteen cities were host to these ceremonies, and the total number attending probably went beyond 100,000.

All these extravaganzas seem to have certain aspects in common aside from their praise of jazz. They differ from most of the other great American fiestas in that they offer no competition, and, therefore, no betting. But they are like the others in their Hollywoodian accent on bigness and bargains. A full-page ad, which ran in a number of magazines, for the first annual Playboy Jazz Festival in Chicago (it was originally scheduled for Soldier Field, but wound up in a slightly less awe-inspiring stadium) announced the event as "Colossal . . . Gigantic . . . The Greatest Jazz Festival on Earth. . . . See and hear more great jazz stars in one weekend than most people see in a lifetime." Newport, too, was always crowded with stars as well as pilgrims, and attempted to offer the fiesta fan everything short of salvation. Last year there was an afternoon of carnival variety in which the crowds had to choose between a regular jazz program at Freebody Park climaxed by a "Jazz Fashion Show," and at the same time, at Rogers High School, the world premiere of a jazz ballet, performed to the music of

John Lewis's *Fontessa,* and based, as the music is,
on the commedia dell' arte. One weary pilgrim returning to his room at the end of the afternoon
speculated that "next year they're going to have a
flood and set it to music."

The Festivals have often been criticized for this
sideshow quality, which sometimes seems to over-
shadow the music, but its backers stoutly defend it
as part of the fiesta nature of the event. (This year
Charlie Mingus and other jazzmen disgruntled by
this carnival aspect put on their own widely praised
festival at Newport's Cliff Walk Manor—with the
assistance of Mrs. Lorillard.) In an article on the
Newport proceedings in *Look,* Maurice Zolotow
wrote that "there is a wonderful atmosphere of re-
lease and fiesta, which, while often experienced in
France, Italy, and Spain, is rarely found in the
United States." I think the observation was valid,
as far as it went, but any comparison with the
European fiestas must end right there. The trim-
mings and presentation of the Newport Festival, and
others like it, are peculiarly American. Can anyone
imagine getting up in the morning after a hard
night of celebrating the running of the bulls in
Pamplona and rushing over to the local school-
house to hear a professor discuss "The Roots of the
Corrida"?

But I joined a faithful group of pilgrims at Newport last summer after a hard night of music and
parties and went to sit in the auditorium of the
local high school to hear Professor Marshall Stearns,
the Cleanth Brooks of the blues, discuss "The Roots
of Jazz." We Americans are not content to dance,
sing, and cavort; we must also dissect. I do not mean
to condemn this national impulse, but it has its sur-
realistic aspects. There was, for instance, the
moment when Professor Stearns was telling us about
the "field hollers" of the Deep South. He explained
that each slave had his own holler, then he put on
a record for illustration. After several scratching
seconds there arose the wail of a human voice:

Oh, Lord, I'm not gonna stay here very long.

You could close your eyes and imagine that God-
forsaken, sun-beaten field and the single figure
standing in it, turning his head toward the blank,
wide sky, and raising that moan from the bottom
of his soul. Then you opened your eyes and there
was the ultramodern, ultrasterile auditorium of
Rogers High School, and the tall, sport-coated professor at the front, lifting the needle from the
record.

Besides the American inclination to study anything we enjoy, Newport's Jazz Festival displays
the bent of our business world for sniffing out anything that smells of life and attempting to suck the
blood for transfusion into its own endeavors. Last
summer's Jazz Fashion Show at Newport was spon-
sored by such enterprises as TWA, Wolfschmidt
vodka, and Studebaker; fashions were chipped in by
American designers. The show, in honor of the
latest product of Studebaker's artisans, was entitled "Newport Is a Lark," and featured one Irene
Zastrow, who was chosen "Golden Lady of Jazz and
Fashion."

What remained of the crowd took the fashion show
with laughs; it was an afternoon crowd, and therefore, by the nature of the Newport proceedings,
more sophisticated. The afternoon programs, which
feature some of the more advanced groups, and
often the best jazz of the festivals, are attended by
much smaller, but much more devoted audiences.
During one of these sessions last summer, one of
the Festival impresarios remarked that "the evening
is more of a social occasion. The real jazz fans come
in the afternoon. And there just aren't that many
real jazz fans."

Fiestas of course are social events, but there are
plenty of social events that fail to strike the public
imagination as Newport does. I think that the music
which lies at the heart of the Festival hullabaloo
has a special pull, particularly now. Jazz is a cult
as well as a kind of music, and it offers the sense of
belonging that any cult does—and a greater measure
than most. During one of the afternoon sessions last

year the drummer Art Blakey came to the micro-
phone and said: "I don't know why there aren't more
of you out there. Next year, bring your square
friends. They're the ones with the bread, anyway.
Get 'em out here and get 'em baptized—they'll love
you for it."

I think he was right, and I think his terms were
right, too. People are not "introduced" to jazz, they
are baptized into it. We already have a man who is
known as the Jazz Priest—Father Norman O'Con-
ner of Boston (not to be confused with piano player
Thelonius Monk, who was introduced to the Newport audience as the High Priest of Jazz).

The notion of jazz as a religion is hard to avoid,
and I think it goes deeper than mere terminology.
The enthusiasm, fervor, and belief of jazz musicians
and listeners is greater than that to be found at any
of our current religious rituals, with the possible
exception of the Pentecostals, whom the "estab-
lished" Protestant leaders look upon as a "fringe
group." Aldous Huxley has suggested that the dying
religions of our time put passion into their proceedings by the use of a drug called mescaline. Perhaps they might try jazz, too, which draws out so
much more genuine emotion than most religious
services.

I was struck by this kind of comparison more
deeply than I ever had been last year at Newport
when I returned from a lively afternoon session of
music and happened to turn on a radio in my hotel
room. The program was the reading of a Catholic
Mass, and a priest was reciting to an answering
chorus the words: "Hail Mary, full of grace . . .
pray for us now and at the hour of our death."

The words were repeated, from priest and chorus,
both of them droning in a singsong monotone. I
listened for a while, fascinated and absorbed in the
compelling monotony of the liturgy, wondering how
many times they would repeat it. It went very fast,
like the reading of an order by a sergeant, and with
roughly the same amount of passion. I tried to take
down the words, but they were spoken too fast and

ran together. I happened to glance down at the desk where I was sitting and noticed a sheet below the glass along the hotel menu, which set forth instructions from Civil Defense to be followed in case of an air raid. It said that this was my home away from home, and that in case of an air raid alarm I should go out into the hall, sit down on the floor with my back against the wall, and await further instructions. It said that I should not attempt to get on the elevator, because only wardens were to use the elevators.

I poured myself a bourbon and water, then put on my tie and walked outside. The sky was that twilight color of blue that Henry James had half a century ago compared to the sky of Venice. Automobiles were moving toward the Festival Park. I followed them, walking down the street that leads off fashionable Bellevue Avenue toward the park. Hundreds of college kids had encamped on the island of grass in the middle of the street, drinking beer, shouting, chasing girls, singing, playing bongo drums, guitars, mandolins, and banjos. A guitar player was being given three "hip-hip-hurrahs" by the crowd around him. They shoved their beer cans up to the evening sky, the silver foam rising and spilling around them.

After the evening program a group of these kids gathered in the shadows outside the Muenchinger-King Hotel, one of them playing a guitar and singing a song about how everyone hates everyone else, and "What nature doesn't do to us, will be done by our fellow man." The last line was: "Someone will set the spark off, and we'll all be blown away."

The next night was Saturday, and Duke Ellington and his band were playing a new composition called "Launching Pad." Toward the end of the program, the great blues singer Jimmy Rushing was called to the stand. I was sitting at the time in one of the boxes, and glanced behind me to watch the crowd as they began to stand, dance, clap, and sway to Rushing's powerful rendition of the blues.

There is a power in the blues, as in the other jazz that has flowed from it, that we have in no other kind of native American art. It is the power of painful honesty, and painful, yet relieving, recognition —recognition of the truth that is denied by the covers of *The Saturday Evening Post* and the lyrics of popular songs that say "the night is like a lovely tune" and "we'll be together again." Jimmy Rushing was telling us

> Walked all night
> Until my feet got wet.
> Walked all night,
> Haven't found my baby yet.
> Bye bye baby, bye bye . . .

The park was alive in front of him, with him, and even in the boxes people were standing up and clapping to the music. It was the kind of revival meeting atmosphere I had expected and failed to find when Billy Graham brought his mild crusade to Madison Square Garden. I happened to be sitting next to Langston Hughes, the poet laureate of Harlem. After saying, with genuine delight, that "you can't beat the blues," he informed me that the man standing up in front of us clapping and blocking the view was Charles McWhorter, legislative assistant to Richard Nixon, and, like Hughes, a member of the Newport board of directors. Jimmy Rushing was singing.

> Don't the moon look lonesome
> Shinin' through the trees . . .

He meant it, too. And the rest of us knew what he meant. To me and Langston Hughes and Charles McWhorter and "Dizzy" Sal of India and Jimmy Rushing of Oklahoma City and Louis Lorillard of Newport and the girls from Vassar and the boys from Sigma Chi; to all of us the moon has looked lonesome shinin' through the trees. And all of us are hungry to hear it.

The crowds that started the riot this year were hungry too. Their pockets may have been full of money and their bellies full of beer, but they were hungry just the same. We have very few opportunities for shouting and singing and letting off steam, and when the chance arrives we hardly know how to act. Walking down the crowded streets of Newport last year where the college kids had gathered to sing and cheer and talk and drink beer, I thought of the lines of the blues that Big Bill Broonzy used to sing, and how much they were all about what was going on:

> I feel like hollerin'
> But the town's too small.

Our town today is the world; it gets smaller all the time, and we have more cause than ever before to feel like hollerin'. There may, of course, not be very much time left to holler, and the grotesque theme that lies beneath all our celebrations is how completely we have come to accept that fact. The women's section of *The New York Times* has instructed us on how to decorate our fallout shelters, and our young sing "folk songs" announcing: "Someone will set the spark off and we'll be blown away." I do not wish to show myself as a crackpot, however, and rather than further pursue this point I will merely follow the current trend and offer a "practical" suggestion. If any descendant of Big Bill Broonzy is around when the spark is finally set off, he might find this slight revision a more appropriate rendition for his blues:

> I feel like hollerin'
> But the town is gone.

THE PORTRAIT OF M. M.

D. H. Lawrence

EDITOR'S NOTE: This little known text was first published as
the preface to *Memoirs of the Foreign Legion*, by "M. M."
The author was one Maurice Magnus, and only the following
facts need to be added to the biographical information given
by Lawrence: In 1915 Magnus joined the French Foreign
Legion. He deserted before seeing combat and crossed the
frontier into Italy. In 1917 Magnus wrote of his adventures
in the Legion, and it was this manuscript, originally entitled *Dregs*, that was published seven years later, with
Lawrence's preface. According to Norman Douglas—the
"N. D." of "The Portrait" and the author of *South Wind*—
Memoirs of the Foreign Legion was considerably expurgated
in its references to what he called "certain ultra-masculine
peculiarities of legionary life." When the book was published,
Douglas attacked Lawrence's preface, claiming that "in ex-
posing the frailties of Maurice Magnus [Lawrence] has con-
trived, like a true Boswell, to expose his own." Such disputes
can no longer move us: Magnus and his book now live only
in Lawrence's first-class epitaph, whose balance of truth and
falsehood is lost in the over-all verity of its character.

On a dark, wet, wintry evening in November 1919,
I arrived in Florence, having just got back to Italy

for the first time since 1914. My wife was in Germany, gone to see her mother, also for the first time since that fatal year 1914. We were poor; who was going to bother to publish me and to pay for my writings, in 1918 and 1919? I landed in Italy with nine pounds in my pocket and about twelve pounds lying in the bank in London. Nothing more. My wife, I hoped, would arrive in Florence with two or three pounds remaining. We should have to go very softly, if we were to house ourselves in Italy for the winter. But after the desperate weariness of the war, one could not bother.

So I had written to N. D. to get me a cheap room somewhere in Florence, and to leave a note at Cook's. I deposited my bit of luggage at the station, and walked to Cook's in the Via Tornabuoni. Florence was strange to me: seemed grim and dark and rather awful on the cold November evening. There was a note from D., who has never left me in the lurch. I went down the Lung' Arno to the address he gave.

I had just passed the end of the Ponte Vecchio, and was watching the first lights of evening and the last light of day on the swollen river as I walked, when I heard D.'s voice:

"Isn't that Lawrence? Why, of course it is, of course it is, beard and all! Well, how are you, eh? You got my note? Well, now, my dear boy, you just go on to the Cavelotti—straight ahead, straight ahead—you've got the number. There's a room for you there. We shall be there in half an hour. Oh, let me introduce you to M."

I had unconsciously seen the two men approaching, D. tall and portly, the other man rather short and strutting. They were both buttoned up in their overcoats, and both had rather curly little hats. But D. was decidedly shabby and a gentleman, with his wicked red face and tufted eyebrows. The other man was almost smart, all in grey, and he looked at first sight like an actor-manager, common. There was a touch of down-on-his-luck about him too. He looked at me, buttoned up in my old thick overcoat, and with my beard bushy and raggy because of my horror of

entering a strange barber's shop, and he greeted me
in a rather fastidious voice, and a little patroniz-
ingly. I forgot to say I was carrying a small handbag. But I realized at once that I ought, in this
little grey-sparrow man's eyes—he stuck his front
out tubbily, like a bird, and his legs seemed to perch
behind him, as a bird's do—I ought to be in a cab.
But I wasn't. He eyed me in that shrewd and rather
impertinent way of the world of actor-managers:
cosmopolitan, knocking shabbily round the world.

He looked a man of about forty, spruce and young-
ish in his deportment, very pink-faced, and very
clean, very natty, very alert, like a sparrow painted
to resemble a tom-tit. He was just the kind of man
I had never met: little smart man of the shabby
world, very much on the spot, don't you know.

"How much does it cost?" I asked D., meaning
the room.

"Oh, my dear fellow, a trifle. Ten francs a day.
Third rate, tenth rate, but not bad at the price.
Pension terms of course—everything included—ex-
cept wine."

"Oh, no, not at all bad for the money," said M.
"Well, now, shall we be moving? You want the post-
office, D.?" His voice was precise and a little minc-
ing, and it had an odd high squeak.

"I do," said D.

"Well, then, come down here—" M. turned to a
dark little alley.

"Not at all," said D. "We turn down by the
bridge."

"This is quicker," said M. He had a twang rather
than an accent in his speech—not definitely American.

He knew all the short cuts of Florence. After-
wards I found that he knew all the short cuts in all
the big towns of Europe.

I went on to the Cavelotti and waited in an awful
plush and gilt drawing-room, and was given at last
a cup of weird muddy brown slush called tea, and a
bit of weird brown mush called jam on some bits
of bread. Then I was taken to my room. It was far

off, on the third floor of the big, ancient, deserted
Florentine house. There I had a big and lonely,
stone-comfortless room looking on to the river. Fortunately it was not very cold inside, and I didn't
care. The adventure of being back in Florence again
after the years of war made one indifferent.

After an hour or so someone tapped. It was D.
coming in with his grandiose air—now a bit shabby,
but still very courtly.

"Why, here you are—miles and miles from human
habitation! I *told* her to put you on the second floor,
were we are. What does she mean by it? Ring the
bell. Ring it."

"No," said I, "I'm all right here."

"What!" cried D. "In this Spitzbergen! Where's
that bell?"

"Don't ring it," said I, who have a horror of
chambermaids and explanations.

"Not ring it! Well, you're a man, you are! Come
on then. Come on down to my room. Come on. Have
you had some tea—filthy muck they call tea here?
I never drink it."

I went down to D.'s room on the lower floor. It
was a littered mass of books and typewriter and
papers: D. was just finishing his novel. M. was resting on the bed, in his shirt sleeves: a tubby, fresh-
faced little man in a suit of grey, faced cloth bound
at the edges with grey silk braid. He had light blue
eyes, tired underneath, and crisp, curly, dark brown
hair just grey at the temples. But everything was
neat and even finicking about his person.

"Sit down! Sit down!" said D., wheeling up a
chair. "Have a whisky?"

"Whisky!" said I.

"Twenty-four francs a bottle—and a find at that,"
moaned D. I must tell that the exchange was then
about forty-five lire to the pound.

"Oh, N.," said M., "I didn't tell you. I was offered
a bottle of 1913 Black and White for twenty-eight
lire."

"Did you buy it?"

"No. It's your turn to buy a bottle."

"Twenty-eight francs—my dear fellow!" said D., cocking up his eyebrows. "I shall have to starve myself to do it."

"Oh, no you won't, you'll eat here just the same," said M.

"Yes, and I'm starved to death. Starved to death by the muck—the absolute muck they call food here. I can't face twenty-eight francs, my dear chap—can't be done, on my honour."

"Well, look here, N. We'll both buy a bottle. And you can get the one at twenty-two, and I'll buy the one at twenty-eight."

So it always was, M. indulged D., and spoilt him in every way. And of course D. wasn't grateful. *Au contraire!* And M.'s pale blue smallish round eyes, in his cockatoo-pink face, would harden to indignation occasionally.

The room was dreadful. D. never opened the windows: didn't believe in opening windows. He believed that a certain amount of nitrogen—I should say a great amount—is beneficial. The queer smell of a bedroom which is slept in, worked in, lived in, smoked in, and in which men drink their whiskies, was something new to me. But I didn't care. One had got away from the war.

We drank our whiskies before dinner. M. was rather yellow under the eyes, and irritable; even his pink fattish face went yellowish.

"Look here," said D. "Didn't you say there was a turkey for dinner? What? Have you been to the kitchen to see what they're doing to it?"

"Yes," said M. testily. "I forced them to prepare it to roast."

"With chestnuts—stuffed with chestnuts?" said D.

"They *said* so," said M.

"Oh, but go down and see that they're doing it. Yes, you've got to keep your eye on them, got to. The most awful howlers if you don't. You go now and see what they're up to." D. used his most irresistible grand manner.

"It's too late," persisted M., testy.

"It's *never* too late. You just run down and absolutely prevent them from boiling that bird in the old soup-water," said D. "If you need force, fetch me."

M. went. He was a great epicure, and knew how things should be cooked. But of course his irruptions into the kitchen roused considerable resentment, and he was getting quaky. However, he went. He came back to say the turkey was being roasted, but without chestnuts.

"What did I tell you! What did I tell you!" cried D. "They are absolute—! If you don't hold them by the neck while they peel the chestnuts, they'll stuff the bird with old boots, to save themselves trouble. Of course, you should have gone down sooner, M."

Dinner was always late, so the whisky was usually two whiskies. Then we went down, and were merry in spite of all things. That is, D. always grumbled about the food. There was one unfortunate youth who was boots and porter and waiter and all. He brought the big dish to D., and D. always poked and pushed among the portions, and grumbled frantically, sotto voce, in Italian to the youth Beppo, getting into a nervous frenzy. Then M. called the waiter to himself, picked the nicest bits off the dish and gave them to D., then helped himself.

The food was not good, but with D. it was an obsession. With the waiter he was terrible. *"Cos' è? Zuppa? Grazie. No, niente per me. No! No! Quest' acqua sporca non bevo io.* I don't drink this dirty water. What—What's that in it—a piece of dish clout? Oh, holy Dio, I can't eat another thing this evening—"

And he yelled for more bread—bread being war-rations and very limited in supply—so M. in nervous distress gave him his piece, and D. threw the crumb part on the floor, anywhere, and called for another litre. We always drank heavy dark red wine at three francs a litre. D. drank two-thirds, M. drank least. He loved his liquors, and did not care for wine. We were noisy and unabashed at table. The old Danish ladies at the other end of the room, and the rather impecunious young Duca and family not far off were not supposed to understand English. The Italians rather liked the noise, and the young signorina with the high-up yellow hair eyed us with profound interest. On we sailed, gay and noisy, D. telling witty anecdotes and grumbling wildly and only half whimsically about the food. We sat on till most people had finished, then went up to more whisky—one more perhaps—in M.'s room.

When I came down in the morning I was called into M.'s room. He was like a little pontiff in a blue kimono-shaped dressing-gown with a broad border of reddish purple: the blue was a soft mid-blue, the material a dull silk. So he minced about, in *demi-toilette*. His room was very clean and neat, and slightly perfumed with essences. On his dressing-table stood many cut-glass bottles and silver-topped bottles with essences and pomades and powders, and heaven knows what. A very elegant little prayer book lay by his bed—and a life of St. Benedict. For M. was a Roman Catholic convert. All he had was expensive and finicking: thick leather silver-studded suit-cases standing near the wall, trouser-stretcher all nice, hair-brushes and clothes-brush with old ivory backs. I wondered over him and his niceties and little pomposities. He was a new bird to me.

For he wasn't at all just the common person he looked. He was queer and sensitive as a woman with D., and patient and fastidious. And yet he *was* common, his very accent was common, and D. despised him.

And M. rather despised me because I did not spend money. I paid for a third of the wine we drank at dinner, and bought the third bottle of whisky we had during M.'s stay. After all, he only stayed three days. But I would not spend for myself. I had no money to spend, since I knew I must live and my wife must live.

"Oh," said M. "Why, that's the very time to spend money, when you've got none. If you've got none, why try to save it? That's been my philosophy all my life; when you've got no money, you may just as well spend it. If you've got a good deal, that's the time to look after it." Then he laughed his queer little laugh, rather squeaky. These were his exact words.

"Precisely," said D. "Spend when you've nothing to spend, my boy. Spent *hard* then."

"No," said I. "If I can help it, I will never let myself be penniless while I live. I mistrust the world too much."

"But if you're going to live in fear of the world," said M., "what's the good of living at all? Might as well die."

I think I give his words almost verbatim. He had a certain impatience of me and of my presence. Yet we had some jolly times—mostly in one or other of their bedrooms, drinking a whisky and talking. We drank a bottle a day—I had very little, preferring the wine at lunch and dinner, which seemed delicious after the war famine. D. would bring up the remains of the second litre in the evening, to go on with before the coffee came.

I arrived in Florence on the Wednesday or Thursday evening; I think Thursday. M. was due to leave for Rome on the Saturday. I asked D. who M. was. "Oh, you never know what he's at. He was manager for Isadora Duncan for a long time—knows all the capitals of Europe: St. Petersburg, Moscow, Tiflis, Constantinople, Berlin, Paris—knows them as you and I know Florence. He's been mostly in that line —theatrical. Then a journalist. He edited the *Roman Review* till the war killed it. Oh, a many-sided sort of fellow."

"But how do you know him?" said I.

"I met him in Capri years and years ago—oh, sixteen years ago—and clean forgot all about him till somebody came to me one day in Rome and said: 'You're N. D.' *I* didn't know who he was. But he'd never forgotten me. Seems to be smitten by me, somehow or other. All the better for me—ha-ha!— if he *likes* to run round for me. My dear fellow, I wouldn't prevent him, if it amuses him. Not for worlds."

And that was how it was. M. ran D.'s errands,

forced the other man to go to the tailor, to the dentist, and was almost a guardian angel to him.

"Look here!" cried D. "I *can't* go to that damned tailor. Let the thing wait, I can't go."

"Oh, yes. Now look here, N., if you don't get it done now while I'm here, you'll never get it done. I made the appointment for three o'clock——"

"To hell with you! Details! Details! I can't stand it, I tell you."

D. chafed and kicked, but went.

"A little fussy fellow," he said. "Oh, yes, fussing about like a woman. Fussy, you know, fussy. I *can't stand* these fussy——" And D. went off into improprieties.

Well, M. ran round and arranged D.'s affairs and settled his little bills, and was so benevolent, and so impatient and nettled at the ungrateful way in which the benevolence was accepted. And D. despised him all the time as a little busybody and an inferior. And I there between them just wondered. It seemed to me M. would get very irritable and nervous at midday and before dinner, yellow around the eyes and played out. He wanted his whisky. He was tired after running round on a thousand errands and quests which I never understood. He always took his morning coffee at dawn, and was out to early Mass and pushing his affairs before eight o'clock in the morning. But what his affairs were I still do not know. Mass is all I am certain of.

However, it was his birthday on the Sunday, and D. would not let him go. He had once said he would give a dinner for his birthday, and this he was not allowed to forget. It seemed to me M. rather wanted to get out of it. But D. was determined to have that dinner.

"You aren't going before you've given us that hare, don't you imagine it, my boy. I've got the smell of that hare in my imagination, and I've damned well got to set my teeth in it. Don't you imagine you're going without having produced that hare."

So poor M., rather a victim, had to consent. We discussed what we should eat. It was decided the hare should have truffles, and a dish of champignons, and cauliflower, and zabaioni—and I forget what else. It was to be on Saturday evening. And M. would leave on Sunday for Rome.

Early on the Saturday morning he went out, with the first daylight, to the old market, to get the hare and the mushrooms. He went himself because he was a connoisseur.

On the Saturday afternoon D. took me wandering round to buy a birthday present.

"I shall have to buy him something—have to—have to—" he said fretfully. He only wanted to spend about five francs. We trailed over the Ponte Vecchio, looking at the jewellers' booths there. It was before the foreigners had come back, and things were still rather dusty and almost at pre-war prices. But we could see nothing for five francs except the little saint-medals. D. wanted to buy one of those. It seemed to me infra dig. So at last coming down to the Mercato Nuovo we saw little bowls of Volterra marble, a natural amber colour, for four francs.

"Look, buy one of those," I said to D., "and he can put his pins or studs or any trifle in, as he needs."

So we went in and bought one of the little bowls of Volterra marble.

M. seemed so touched and pleased with the gift.

"Thank you a thousand times, N.," he said. "That's charming! That's exactly what I want."

The dinner was quite a success, and, poorly fed as we were at the pension, we stuffed ourselves tight on the mushrooms and the hare and the zabaioni, and drank ourselves tight with the good red wine which swung in its straw flask in the silver swing on the table. A flask has two and a quarter litres. We were four persons, and we drank almost two flasks. D. made the waiter measure the remaining half-litre and take it off the bill. But good, good food, and cost about twelve francs a head the whole dinner.

Well, next day was nothing but bags and suit-cases in M.'s room, and the misery of departure with

luggage. He went on the midnight train to Rome—
first class.

"I always travel first class," he said, "and I always shall, while I can buy the ticket. Why should
I go second? It's beastly enough to travel at all."

"My dear fellow, I came up third the last time I
came from Rome," said D. "Oh, not bad, not bad.
Damned fatiguing journey anyhow."

So the little outsider was gone, and I was rather
glad. I don't think he liked me. Yet one day he said
to me at table:

"How lovely your hair is—such a lovely colour!
What do you dye it with?"

I laughed, thinking he was laughing too. But no,
he meant it.

"It's got no particular colour at all," I said, "so I
couldn't dye it that!"

"It's a lovely colour," he said. And I think he
didn't believe me, that I didn't dye it. It puzzled me,
and it puzzles me still.

But he was gone. D. moved into M.'s room, and
asked me to come down to the room he himself was
vacating. But I preferred to stay upstairs.

M. was a fervent Catholic, taking the religion,
alas, rather unctuously. He had entered the Church
only a few years before. But he had a bishop for a
god-father, and seemed to be very intimate with
the upper clergy. He was very pleased and proud
because he was a constant guest at the famous old
monastery south of Rome. He talked of becoming a
monk, a monk in that aristocratic and well-bred
order. But he had not even begun his theological
studies: or any studies of any sort. And D. said he
only chose the Benedictines because they lived better
than any of the others.

But I had said to M., that when my wife came and
we moved south, I would like to visit the monastery
some time, if I might. "Certainly," he said. "Come
when I am there. I shall be there in about a month's
time. Do come! Do be sure and come. It's a wonderful place—oh, wonderful. It will make a great impression on you. Do come. Do come. And I will tell

Don Bernardo, who is my *greatest* friend, and who is guest-master, about you. So that if you wish to go when I am not there, write to Don Bernardo. But do come when I am there."

My wife and I were due to go into the mountains south of Rome, and stay there some months. Then I was to visit the big, noble monastery that stands on a bluff hill like a fortress crowning a great precipice, above the little town and the plain between the mountains. But it was so icy cold and snowy among the mountains, it was unbearable. We fled south again, to Naples, and to Capri. Passing, I saw the monastery crouching there above, world-famous, but it was impossible to call then.

I wrote and told M. of my move. In Capri I had an answer from him. It had a wistful tone—and I don't know what made me think that he was in trouble, in monetary difficulty. But felt it acutely—a kind of appeal. Yet he said nothing direct. And he wrote from an expensive hotel in Anzio, on the sea near Rome.

At the moment I had just received twenty pounds, unexpected and joyful, from America—a gift too. I hesitated for some time, because I felt unsure. Yet the curious appeal came out of the letter, though nothing was said. And I felt also I owed M. that dinner, and I didn't want to owe him anything, since he despised me a little for being careful. So partly out of revenge, perhaps, and partly because I felt the strange wistfulness of him appealing to me, I sent him five pounds, saying perhaps I was mistaken in imagining him very hard up, but if so, he wasn't to be offended.

It is strange to me even now, how I knew he was appealing to me. Because it was all as vague as I say. Yet I felt it so strongly. He replied: "Your cheque has saved my life. Since I last saw you I have fallen down an abyss. But I will tell you when I see you. I shall be at the monastery in three days. Do come—and come alone." I have forgotten to say that he was a rabid woman-hater.

This was just after Christmas. I thought his

"saved my life" and "fallen down an abyss" was just the American touch of "very, very—" I wondered what on earth the abyss could be, and I decided it must be that he had lost his money or his hopes. It seemed to me that some of his old buoyant assurance came out again in this letter. But he was now very friendly, urging me to come to the monastery, and treating me with a curious little tenderness and protectiveness. He had a queer delicacy of his own, varying with a bounce and a commonness. He was a common little bounder. And then he had this curious delicacy and tenderness and wistfulness.

I put off going north. I had another letter urging me—and it seemed to me that, rather assuredly, he was expecting more money. Rather cockily, as if he had a right to it. And that made me not want to give him any. Besides, as my wife said, what right had I to give away the little money we had, and we there stranded in the south of Italy with no resources if once we were spent up? And I have always been determined *never* to come to my last shilling—if I have to reduce my spending almost to nothingness. I have always been determined to keep a few pounds between me and the world.

I did not send any money. But I wanted to go to the monastery, so wrote and said I would come for two days. I always remember getting up in the black dark of the January morning, and making a little coffee on the spirit-lamp, and watching the clock, the big-faced, blue old clock on the campanile in the piazza in Capri, to see I wasn't late. The electric light in the piazza lit up the face of the campanile. And we were then, a stone's throw away, high in the Palazzo Ferraro, opposite the bubbly roof of the little *duomo*. Strange dark winter morning, with the open sea beyond the roofs, seen through the side window, and the thin line of the lights of Naples twinkling far, far off.

At ten minutes to six I went down the smelly dark stone stairs of the old palazzo, out into the street. A few people were already hastening up the street to the terrace that looks over the sea to the bay of

Naples. It was dark and cold. We slid down in the funicular to the shore, then in little boats were rowed out over the dark sea to the steamer that lay there showing her lights and hooting.

It was three long hours across the sea to Naples, with dawn coming slowly in the East, beyond Ischia, and flushing into lovely colours as our steamer pottered along the peninsula, calling at Massa and Sorrento and Piano. I always loved hanging over the side and watching the people come out in boats from the little places of the shore, that rose steep and beautiful. I love the movement of these watery, Neapolitan people, and the naïve trustful way they clamber in and out the boats, and their softness, and their dark eyes. But when the steamer leaves the peninsula and begins to make away round Vesuvius to Naples, one is already tired, and cold, cold, cold in the wind that comes piercing from the snow-crests away there along Italy. Cold, and reduced to a kind of stony apathy by the time we come to the mole in Naples, at ten o'clock—or twenty past ten.

We were rather late, and I missed the train. I had to wait till two o'clock. And Naples is a hopeless town to spend three hours in. However, time passes. I remember I was calculating in my mind whether they had given me the right change at the ticket-window. They hadn't—and I hadn't counted in time. Thinking of this, I got in the Rome train. I had been there ten minutes when I heard a trumpet blow.

"Is this the Rome train?" I asked my fellow-traveller.

"*Sì.*"

"The express?"

"No, it is the slow train."

"It leaves?"

"At ten past two."

I almost jumped through the window. I flew down the platform.

"The *diretto!*" I cried to a porter.

"*Parte! Eccolo la!*" he said, pointing to a big train moving inevitably away.

I flew with wild feet across the various railway

lines and seized the end of the train as it travelled. I had caught it. Perhaps if I had missed it fate would have been different. So I sat still for about three hours. Then I had arrived.

There is a long drive up the hill from the station to the monastery. The driver talked to me. It was evident he bore the monks no good will.

"Formerly," he said, "if you went up to the monastery you got a glass of wine and a plate of macaroni. But now they kick you out of the door."

"Do they?" I said. "It is hard to believe."

"They kick you out of the gate," he vociferated.

We twisted up and up the wild hillside, past the old castle of the town, past the last villa, between trees and rocks. We saw no one. The whole hill belongs to the monastery. At last at twilight we turned the corner of the oak wood and saw the monastery like a huge square fortress-palace of the sixteenth century crowning the near distance. Yes, and there was M. just stepping through the huge old gateway and hastening down the slope to where the carriage must stop. He was bareheaded, and walking with his perky, busy little stride, seemed very much at home in the place. He looked up to me with a tender, intimate look as I got down from the carriage. Then he took my hand.

"So *very* glad to see you," he said. "I'm so *pleased* you've come."

And he looked into my eyes with that wistful, watchful tenderness rather like a woman who isn't quite sure of her lover. He had a certain charm in his manner; and an odd pompous touch with it at this moment, welcoming his guest at the gate of the vast monastery which reared above us from its buttresses in the rock, was rather becoming. His face was still pink, his eyes pale blue and sharp, but he looked greyer at the temples.

"Give me your bag," he said. "Yes, do—and come along. Don Bernardo is just at Evensong, but he'll be here in a little while. Well, now, tell me all the news."

"Wait," I said. "Lend me five francs to finish paying the driver—he has no change."

"Certainly, certainly," he said, giving the five francs.

I had no news, so asked him his.

"Oh, I have none either," he said. "Very short of money, that of course is *no* news." And he laughed his little laugh. "I'm so glad to be here," he continued. "The peace, and the rhythm of the life is so *beautiful!* I'm sure you'll love it."

We went up the slope under the big, tunnel-like entrance and were in the grassy courtyard, with the arched walk on the far sides, and one or two trees. It was like a grassy cloister, but still busy. Black monks were standing chatting, an old peasant was just driving two sheep from the cloister grass, and an old monk was darting into the little post-office which one recognized by the shield with the national arms over the doorway. From under the far arches came an old peasant carrying a two-handed saw.

And there was Don Bernardo, a tall monk in a black, well-shaped gown, young, good-looking, gentle, hastening forward with a quick smile. He was about my age, and his manner seemed fresh and subdued, as if he were still a student. One felt one was at college with one's college mates.

We went up the narrow stair and into the long, old, naked white corridor, high and arched. Don Bernardo had got the key of my room: two keys, one for the dark antechamber, one for the bedroom. A charming and elegant bedroom, with an engraving of English landscape, and outside the net curtain a balcony looking down on the garden, a narrow strip beneath the walls, and beyond, the clustered buildings of the farm, and the oak woods and arable fields of the hill summit; and beyond again, the gulf where the world's valley was, and all the mountains that stand in Italy on the plains as if God had just put them down ready made. The sun had already sunk, the snow on the mountains was full of a rosy glow, the valleys were full of shadow. One heard, far below, the trains shunting, the world clinking in the cold air.

"Isn't it wonderful! Ah, the most wonderful place on earth!" said M. "What now could you wish better than to end your days here? The peace, the beauty, the eternity of it." He paused and sighed. Then he put his hand on Don Bernardo's arm and smiled at him with that odd, rather wistful smirking tenderness that made him such a quaint creature in my eyes.

"But I'm going to enter the order. You're going to let me be a monk and be one of you, aren't you, Don Bernardo?"

"We will see," smiled Don Bernardo. "When you have begun your studies."

"It will take me two years," said M. "I shall have to go to college in Rome. When I have got the money for the fees—" He talked away, like a boy planning a new role.

"But I'm sure Lawrence would like to drink a cup of tea," said Don Bernardo. He spoke English as if it were his native language. "Shall I tell them to make it in the kitchen, or shall we go to your room?"

"Oh, we'll go to my room. How thoughtless of me! Do forgive me, won't you?" said M., laying his hand gently on my arm. "I'm so awfully sorry, you know. But we get so excited and enchanted when we talk of the monastery. But come along, come along, it will be ready in a moment on the spirit-lamp."

We went down to the end of the high, white, naked corridor. M. had a quite sumptuous room, with a curtained bed in one part, and under the window his writing-desk with papers and photographs, and near by a sofa and an easy table, making a little sitting-room, while the bed and toilet things, pomades and bottles, were all in the distance, in the shadow. Night was fallen. From the window one saw the world far below, like a pool the flat plain, a deep pool of darkness with little twinkling lights, and rows and bunches of light that were the railway station.

I drank my tea, M. drank a little liqueur, Don

Bernardo in his black winter robe sat and talked
with us. At least he did very little talking. But he
listened and smiled and put in a word or two as we
talked, seated round the table on which stood the
green-shaded electric lamp.

The monastery was cold as the tomb. Couched
there on the top of its hill, it is not much below the
winter snow-line. Now by the end of January all the
summer heat is soaked out of the vast, ponderous
stone walls, and they become masses of coldness
cloaking around. There is no heating apparatus
whatsoever—none. Save the fire in the kitchen, for
cooking, nothing. Dead, silent, stone cold everywhere.

At seven we went down to dinner. Capri in the
daytime was hot, so I had brought only a thin old
dust-coat. M. therefore made me wear a big coat
of his own, a coat made of thick, smooth black cloth,
and lined with black sealskin, and having a collar of
silky black sealskin. I can still remember the feel of
the silky fur. It was queer to have him helping me
solicitously into this coat, and buttoning it at the
throat for me.

"Yes, it's a beautiful coat. Of course!" he said. "I
hope you find it warm."

"Wonderful," said I. "I feel as warm as a millionaire."

"I'm so glad you do," he laughed.

"You don't mind my wearing your grand coat?"
I said.

"Of course not! Of course not! It's a pleasure to
me if it will keep you warm. We don't want to die
of cold in the monastery, do we? That's one of the
mortifications we will do our best to avoid. What?
Don't you think? Yes, I think this coldness is going
almost too far. I had that coat made in New York
fifteen years ago. Of course in Italy" he said It'ly—
"I've never worn it, so it is as good as new. And it's
a beautiful coat, fur and cloth of the very best. *And*
the tailor." He laughed a little, self-approving laugh.
He liked to give the impression that he dealt with
the *best* shops, don't you know, and stayed in the

best hotels, etc. I grinned inside the coat, detesting
best hotels, best shops, and best overcoats. So off we
went, he in his grey overcoat and I in my sealskin
millionaire monster, down the dim corridor to the
guests' refectory. It was a bare room with a long
white table. M. and I sat at the near end. Further
down was another man, perhaps the father of one of
the boy students. There is a college attached to the
monastery.

We sat in the icy room, muffled up in our overcoats. A lay brother with a bulging forehead and
queer, fixed eyes waited on us. He might easily have
come from an old Italian picture. One of the adoring
peasants. The food was abundant—but, alas, it had
got cold in the long cold transit from the kitchen.
And it was roughly cooked, even if it was quite
wholesome. Poor M. did not eat much, but nervously
nibbled his bread. I could tell the meals were a trial
to him. He could not bear the cold food in that icy,
empty refectory. And his tisickiness offended the lay
brothers. I could see that his little pomposities and
his "superior" behaviour and his long stay made
them have that old monastic grudge against him,
silent but very obstinate and effectual—the same
now as six hundred years ago. We had a decanter
of good red wine—but he did not care for much
wine. He was glad to be peeling the cold orange
which was dessert.

After dinner he took me down to see the church,
creeping like two thieves down the dimness of the
great, prison-cold white corridors, on the cold flag
floors. Stone-cold: the monks must have invented the
term. These monks were at Complin. So we went
by our two secret little selves into the tall dense
nearly-darkness of the church. M., knowing his way
about here as in the cities, led me, poor wondering
worldling, by the arm through the gulfs of the tomb-
like place. He found the electric light switches inside
the church, and stealthily made me a light as we
went. We looked at the lily marble of the great floor,
at the pillars, at the Benvenuto Cellini casket, at the
really lovely pillars and slabs of different coloured

marbles, yellow and grey and rose and green and lily-white, veined and mottled and splashed: lovely, lovely stones— And Benvenuto had used pieces of lapis lazuli, blue as cornflowers. Yes, yes, all very rich and wonderful.

We tiptoed about the dark church stealthily, from altar to altar, and M. whispered ecstasies in my ear. Each time we passed before an altar, whether the high altar or the side chapels, he did a wonderful reverence, which he must have practised for hours, bowing waxily down and sinking till his one knee touched the pavement, then rising like a flower that rises and unfolds again, till he had skipped to my side and was playing cicerone once more. Always in his grey overcoat, and in whispers; me in the black overcoat, millionarish. Se we crept into the chancel and examined all the queer fat babies of the choir stalls, carved in wood and rolling on their little backs between monk's place and monk's place— queer things for the chanting monks to have between them, these shiny, polished, dark brown fat babies, all different, and all jolly and lusty. We looked at everything in the church—and then at everything in the ancient room at the side where surplices hang and monks can wash their hands.

Then we went down to the crypt, where the modern mosaics glow in wonderful colours, and sometimes in fascinating little fantastic trees and birds. But it was rather like a scene in a theatre, with M. for the wizard and myself a sort of Parsifal in the New York coat. He switched on the lights, the gold mosaic of the vaulting glittered and bowed, the blue mosaic glowed out, the holy of holies gleamed theatrically, the stiff mosaic figures posed around us. To tell the truth, I was glad to get back to the normal human room and sit on a sofa huddled in my overcoat, and look at photographs which M. showed me: photographs of everywhere in Europe. Then he showed me a wonderful photograph of a picture of a lovely lady, asked me what I thought of it, and seemed to expect me to be struck to bits by the beauty. His almost sanctimonious expectation made me tell the truth, that I thought it just a bit cheap, trivial. And then he said, dramatic:

"That's my mother."

It looked so unlike anybody's mother, much less M.'s, that I was startled. I realized that she was his great stunt, and that I had put my foot in it. So I just held my tongue. Then I said, for I felt he was going to be silent forever:

"There are so few portraits, unless by the really great artists, that aren't a bit cheap. She must have been a beautiful woman."

"Yes, she *was*," he said curtly. And we dropped the subject.

He locked all his drawers *very* carefully, and kept the keys on a chain. He seemed to give the impression that he had a great many secrets, perhaps dangerous ones, locked up in the drawers of his writing-table there. And I always wonder what the secrets can be, that are able to be kept so tight under lock and key.

Don Bernardo tapped and entered. We all sat round and sipped a funny liqueur which I didn't like. M. lamented that the bottle was finished. I asked him to order another and let me pay for it. So he said he would tell the postman to bring it up next day from the town. Don Bernardo sipped his tiny glass with the rest of us, and he told me, briefly, his story—and we talked politics till nearly midnight. Then I came out of the black overcoat and we went to bed.

In the morning a fat, smiling, nice old lay brother brought me my water. It was a sunny day. I looked down on the farm cluster and the brown fields and the sere oak woods of the hill-crown, and the rocks and bushes savagely bordering it round. Beyond, the mountains with their snow were blue-glistery with sunshine, and seemed quite near, but across a sort of gulf. All was still and sunny. And the poignant grip of the past, the grandiose, violent past of the Middle Ages, when blood was strong and unquenched and life was flamboyant with splendours and horrible miseries, took hold of me till I could hardly bear it. It was really agony to me to be in the monastery and to see the old farm and the bullocks slowly working in the fields below, and the black pigs rooting among weeds, and to see a monk sitting on a parapet in the sun, and an old, old man in skin sandals and white bunched, swathed legs come driving an ass slowly to the monastery gate, slowly, with all that lingering nonchalance and wildness of the Middle Ages, and yet to know that I was myself, child of the present. It was so strange from M.'s window to look down on the plain and see the white road going straight past a mountain that stood like a loaf of sugar, the river meandering in loops, and the railway with glistening lines making a long black swoop across the flat and into the hills. To see trains come steaming, with white smoke flying. To see the station like a little harbour where trucks like shipping stood anchored in rows in the black bay of railway. To see trains stop in the station and tiny people swarming like flies! To see all this from the monastery, where the Middle Ages live on in a sort of agony, like Tithonus, and cannot die, this was almost a violation to my soul, made almost a wound.

Immediately after coffee we went down to Mass. It was celebrated in a small crypt chapel underground, because that was warmer. The twenty or so monks sat in their stalls, one monk officiating at the altar. It was quiet and simple, the monks sang sweetly and well, there was no organ. It seemed soon to pass by. M. and I sat near the door. He was very devoted and scrupulous in his going up and down. I was an outsider. But it was pleasant—not too sacred. One felt the monks were very human in their likes and their jealousies. It was rather like a group of dons in the dons' room at Cambridge, a cluster of professors in any college. But during Mass they, of course, just sang their responses. Only I could tell some watched the officiating monk rather with ridicule—he was one of the ultra-punctilious

sort, just like a don. And some boomed their responses with a grain of defiance against some
brother monk who had earned dislike. It was human,
and more like a university than anything. We went
to Mass every morning, but I did not go to Evensong.

After Mass, M. took me round and showed me
everything of the vast monastery. We went into the
Bramante Courtyard, all stone, with its great well in
the centre, and the colonnades of arches going round,
full of sunshine, gay and Renaissance, a little bit
ornate but still so jolly and gay, sunny pale stone
waiting for the lively people, with the great flight
of pale steps sweeping up to the doors of the church,
waiting for gentlemen in scarlet trunk-hose, slender
red legs, and ladies in brocade gowns, and page-boys
with fluffed golden hair. Splendid, sunny, gay Bramante Courtyard of lively stone. But empty. Empty
of life. The gay red-legged gentry dead for ever. And
when pilgrimages do come and throng in, it is
horrible artisan excursions from the great town, and
the sordidness of industrialism.

We climbed the little watchtower that is now an
observatory, and saw the vague and unshaven Don
Giovanni among all his dust and instruments. M.
was very familiar and friendly, chattering in his
quaint Italian, which was more wrong than any
Italian I have ever heard spoken; very familiar and
friendly, and a tiny bit deferential to the monks, and
yet, and yet—rather patronizing. His little pomposity and patronizing tone coloured even his deferential yearning to be admitted to the monastery.
The monks were rather brief with him. They no
doubt have their likes and dislikes greatly intensified
by the monastic life.

We stood on the summit of the tower and looked at
the world below: the town, the castle, the white
roads coming straight as judgment out of the
mountains north, from Rome, and piercing into the
mountains south, toward Naples, traversing the
flat, flat plain. Roads, railway, river, streams, a
world in accurate and lively detail, with mountains
sticking up abruptly and rockily, as the old painters

painted it. I think there is no way of painting Italian landscape except that way—that started with Loren-zetti and ended with the sixteenth century.

We looked at the ancient cell away under the monastery, where all the sanctity started. We looked at the big library that belongs to the State, and at the smaller library that belongs still to the abbot. I was tired, cold, and sick among the books and illuminations. I could not bear it any more. I felt I must be outside, in the sun, and see the world below, and the way out.

That evening I said to M.:

"And what was the abyss, then?"

"Oh, well, you know," he said, "it was a cheque which I made out at Anzio. There should have been money to meet it, in my bank in New York. But it appears the money had never been paid in by the people that owed it me. So there was I in a very nasty hole, an unmet cheque, and no money at all in Italy. I really had to escape here. It is an *absolute* secret that I am here, and it must be, till I can get this business settled. Of course I've written to America about it. But as you see, I'm in a very nasty hole. That five francs I gave you for the driver was the last penny I had in the world: absolutely the last penny. I haven't even anything to buy a cigarette or a stamp." And he laughed chirpily, as if it were a joke. But he didn't really think it a joke. Nor was it a joke.

I had come with only two hundred lire in my pocket, as I was waiting to change some money at the bank. Of this two hundred I had one hundred left or one hundred and twenty-five. I should need a hundred to get home. I could only give M. the twenty-five, for the bottle of drink. He was rather crestfallen. But I didn't want to give him money this time—because he expected it.

However, we talked about his plans: how he was to earn something. He told me what he had written. And I cast over in my mind where he might get something published in London, wrote a couple of letters on his account, told him where I thought he

had best send his material. There wasn't a great deal
of hope, for his smaller journalistic articles seemed
to me very self-conscious and poor. He had one
about the monastery, which I thought he might sell
because of the photographs.

That evening he first showed me the Legion manuscript. He had got it rather raggedly typed out. He
had a typewriter, but he felt he ought to have somebody to do his typing for him, as he hated it and
did unwillingly. That evening and when I went to
bed and when I woke in the morning I read this
manuscript. It did not seem very good—vague and
diffuse where it shouldn't have been—lacking in
sharp detail and definite event. And yet there was
something in it that made me want it done properly.
So we talked about it, and discussed it carefully, and
he unwillingly promised to tackle it again. He was
curious, always talking about his work, even always
working, but never *properly* doing anything.

We walked out in the afternoon through the woods
and across the rocky bit of moorland which covers
most of the hill-top. We were going to the ruined
convent which lies on the other brow of the monastery hill, abandoned and sad among the rocks and
heath and thorny bushes. It was sunny and warm.
A barefoot little boy was tending a cow and three
goats and a pony, a barefoot little girl had five geese
in charge. We came to the convent and looked in.
The further part of the courtyard was still entire,
the place was a sort of farm, two rooms occupied
by a peasant-farmer. We climbed about the ruins.
Some creature was crying—crying, crying, crying
with a strange, inhuman persistence, leaving off and
crying again. We listened and listened—the sharp,
poignant crying. Almost it might have been a sharp-
voiced baby. We scrambled about, looking. And at
last outside a little cave-like place found a blind
black puppy crawling miserably on the floor, unable
to walk, and crying incessantly. We put it back in the
little cave-like shed, and went away. The place was
deserted save for the crying puppy.

On the road outside, however, was a man, a peasant, just drawing up to the arched convent gateway with an ass under a load of brushwood. He was thin and black and dirty. He took off his hat, and we told him of the puppy. He said the bitch-mother had gone off with his son with the sheep. Yes, she had been gone all day. Yes, she would be back at sunset. No, the puppy had not drunk all day. Yes, the little beast cried, but the mother would come back to him.

They were the Old World peasants still about the monastery, with the hard, small bony heads and deep-lined faces and utterly blank minds, crying their speech as crows cry, and living their lives as lizards among the rocks, blindly going on with the little job in hand, the present moment cut off from all past and future, and having no idea and no sustained emotion, only that eternal will-to-live which makes a tortoise wake up once more in spring, and makes a grasshopper whistle on in the moonlight nights even of November. Only these peasants don't whistle much. The whistlers go to America. It is the hard, static, unhoping souls that persist in the old life. And still they stand back, as one passes them in the corridors of the great monastery, they press themselves back against the whitewashed walls of the still place, and drop their heads, as if some mystery were passing by, some God-mystery, the higher beings, which they must not look closely upon. So also this old peasant—he was not old, but deep-lined like a gnarled bough. He stood with his hat down in his hands as we spoke to him and answered short, hard, insentient answers, as a tree might speak.

"The monks keep their peasants humble," I said to M.

"Of course!" he said. "Don't you think they are quite right? Don't you think they should be humble?" And he bridled like a little turkey-cock on his hind legs.

"Well," I said, "if there's any occasion for humility, I do."

"Don't you think there is occasion?" he cried. "If

there's one thing worse than another, it's this *equality* that has come into the world. Do you believe in it yourself?"

"No," I said. "I don't believe in equality. But the problem is, wherein does superiority lie?"

"Oh," chirped M. complacently. "It lies in many things. It lies in birth and upbringing and so on, but it is chiefly in *mind*. Don't you think? Of course I don't mean that the physical qualities aren't *charming*. They are, and nobody appreciates them more than I do. Some of the peasants are *beautiful* creatures, perfectly beautiful. But that passes. And the mind endures."

I did not answer. M. was not a man one talked far with. But I thought to myself, I *could* not accept M.'s superiority to the peasant. If I had really to live always under the same roof with either one of them, I would have chosen the peasant. Not because the peasant was wonderful and stored with mystic qualities. No, I don't give much for the wonderful mystic qualities in peasants. Money is their mystery of mysteries, absolutely. No, if I chose the peasant it would be for what he *lacked* rather than for what he had. He lacked that complacent mentality that M. was so proud of, he lacked all the trivial trash of glib talk and more glib thought, all the conceit of our shallow consciousness. For his mindlessness I would have chosen the peasant, and for his strong blood-presence. M. wearied me with his facility and his readiness to rush into speech, and for the exhaustive nature of his presence. As if he had no strong blood in him to sustain him, only this modern parasitic lymph which cries for sympathy all the time.

"Don't you think yourself that you are superior to that peasant?" he asked me, rather ironically. He half expected me to say no.

"Yes, I do," I replied. "But I think most middle-class, most so-called educated people are inferior to the peasant. I do that."

"Of course," said M. readily. "In their *hypocrisy* —" He was great against hypocrisy—especially the English sort.

"And if I think myself superior to the peasant, it is only that I feel myself like the growing tip, or one of the growing tips of the tree, and him like a piece of the hard, fixed tissue of the branch or trunk. We're part of the same tree: and it's the same sap," said I.

"Why, exactly! Exactly!" cried M. "Of course! The Church would teach the same doctrine. We are all one in Christ—but between our souls and our duties there are great differences."

It is terrible to be agreed with, especially by a man like M. All that one says, and means, turns to nothing.

"Yes," I persisted. "But it seems to me the so-called culture, education, the so-called leaders and leading-classes today, are only parasites—like a great flourishing bush of parasitic consciousness flourishing on top of the tree of life, and sapping it. The consciousness of today doesn't rise from the roots. It is just parasitic in the veins of life. And the middle and upper classes are just parasitic upon the body of life which still remains in the lower classes."

"What!" said M. acidly. "Do you believe in the democratic lower classes?"

"Not a bit," said I.

"I should think not, indeed!" he cried complacently.

"No, I don't believe the lower classes can ever make life whole again, till they *do* become humble, like the old peasants, and yield themselves to real leaders. But not to great negators like Lloyd George or Lenin or Briand."

"Of course! Of course!" he cried. "What you need is the Church in power again. The Church has a place for everybody."

"You don't think the Church belongs to the past?" I asked.

"Indeed I don't, or I shouldn't be here. No," he said sententiously, "the Church is eternal. It puts people in their proper place. It puts women down into *their* proper place, which is the first thing to be done——"

He had a great dislike of women, and was very acid about them. Not because of their sins, but because of their virtues: their economies, their philanthropies, their spiritualities. Oh, how he loathed women! He had been married, but the marriage had not been a success. He smarted still. Perhaps his wife had despised him, and he had not *quite* been able to defeat her contempt.

So he loathed women, and wished for a world of men. "They talk about love between men and women," he said. "Why, it's all a *fraud*. The woman is just taking all and giving nothing, and feeling sanctified about it. All she tries to do is thwart a man in whatever he is doing. No, I have found my life in my *friendships*. Physical relationships are very attractive, of course, and one tries to keep them as decent and all that as one can. But one knows they will pass and be finished. But one's *mental* friendships last forever."

"With me, on the contrary," said I. "If there is no profound blood-sympathy, I know the mental friendship is trash. If there is real, deep blood-response, I will stick to that if I have to betray all the mental sympathies I ever made, or all the lasting spiritual loves I ever felt."

He looked at me, and his face seemed to fall. Round the eyes he was yellow and tired and nervous. He watched me for some time.

"Oh!" he said, in a queer tone, rather cold. "Well, my experience has been the opposite."

We were silent for some time.

"And you," I said, "even if you do manage to do all your studies and enter the monastery, do you think you will be satisfied?"

"If I can be so fortunate, I do really," he said. "Do you doubt it?"

"Yes," I said. "Your nature is worldly, more worldly than mine. Yet I should die if I had to stay up here."

"Why?" he asked, curiously.

"Oh, I don't know. The past, the past. The beautiful, the wonderful past, it seems to prey on my heart, I can't bear it."

He watched me closely.

"Really!" he said stoutly. "Do you feel like that? But don't you think it is a far preferable life up here than down there? Don't you think the past is far preferable to the future, with all this *socialismo* and these *communisti* and so on?"

We were seated, in the sunny afternoon, on the wild hill-top high above the world. Across the stretch of pale, dry, standing thistles that peopled the waste ground, and beyond the rocks was the ruined convent. Rocks rose behind us, the summit. Away on the left were the woods which hid us from the great monastery. This was the mountain top, the last foothold of the old world. Below we could see the plain, the straight white road, straight as a thought, and the more flexible black railway with the railway station. There swarmed the *ferrovieri* like ants. There was democracy, industrialism, socialism, the red flag of the communists and the red, white, and green tricolour of the fascisti. That was another world. And how bitter, how barren a world! Barren, like the black cinder-track of the railway, with its two steel lines.

And here above, sitting with the little stretch of pale, dry thistles around us, our back to a warm rock, we were in the Middle Ages. Both worlds were agony to me. But here, on the mountain top, was worst: the past, the poignancy of the not-quite-dead past.

"I think one's got to go through with the life down there—get somewhere beyond it. One can't go back," I said to him.

"But do you call the monastery going back?" he said. "I don't. The peace, the eternity, the concern with things that matter. I consider it the happiest fate that could happen to me. Of course it means putting physical things aside. But when you've done that—why, it seems to me perfect."

"No," I said. "You're too worldly."

"But the monastery is worldly too. We're not Trappists. Why, the monastery is one of the centres of the world—one of the most active centres."

"Maybe. But that impersonal activity, with the blood suppressed and going sour—no, it's too late. It is too abstract—political maybe——"

"I'm sorry you think so," he said, rising. "I don't."

"Well," I said. "You'll never be a monk here, M. You see if you are."

"You don't think I shall?" he replied, turning to me. And there was a catch of relief in his voice. Really, the monastic state must have been like going to prison for him.

"You haven't a vocation," I said.

"I may not *seem* to have, but I hope I actually have."

"You haven't."

"Of course, if you're so sure," he laughed, putting his hand on my arm.

He seemed to understand so much, round about the questions that trouble one deepest. But the quick of the question he never felt. He had no real middle, no real centre bit to him. Yet, round and round about all the questions, he was so intelligent and sensitive.

We went slowly back. The peaks of those Italian mountains in the sunset, the extinguishing twinkle of the plain away below, as the sun declined and grew yellow; the intensely powerful medieval spirit lingering on this wild hill summit, all the wonder of the medieval past; and then the huge mossy stones in the wintry wood that was once a sacred grove; the ancient path through the wood that led from temple to temple on the hill summit, before Christ was born; and then the great Cyclopean wall one passes at the bend of the road, built even before the pagan temples; all this overcame me so powerfully this afternoon, that I was almost speechless. That hill-top must have been one of man's intensely sacred places for three thousand years. And men die generation after generation, races die, but the new cult finds root in the old sacred place, and the quick spot of earth dies very slowly. Yet at last it too dies. But this quick spot is still not quite dead. The great monastery couchant there, half empty, but also not quite dead. And M. and I walking across as the sun set yellow and the cold of the snow came into the air, back home to the monastery! And I feeling as if my heart had once more broken—I don't know why. And he feeling his fear of life, that haunted him, and his fear of his own self and its consequences, that never left him for long. And he seemed to walk close to me, very close. And we had neither of us anything more to say.

Don Bernardo was looking for us as we came up under the archway, he hatless in the cold evening, his black dress swinging voluminous. There were letters for M. There was a small cheque for him from America—about fifty dollars—from some newspaper in the Middle West that had printed one of his articles. He had to talk with Don Bernardo about this.

I decided to go back the next day. I could not stay any longer. M. was very disappointed, and begged me to remain. "I thought you would stay a week at least," he said. "Do stay over Sunday. Oh, do!" But I couldn't, I didn't want to. I could see that his days were a torture to him—the long, cold days in that vast quiet building, with the strange and exhausting silence in the air, and the sense of the past preying on one, and the sense of the silent, suppressed scheming struggle of life going on still in the sacred place.

It was a cloudy morning. In the green courtyard the big Don Anselmo had just caught the little Don Lorenzo round the waist and was swinging him over a bush, like lads before school. The prior was just hurrying somewhere, following his long fine nose. He bade me good-bye; pleasant, warm, jolly, with a touch of wistfulness in his deafness. I parted with real regret from Don Bernardo.

M. was coming with me down the hill—not down the carriage road, but down the wide old paved path that swoops so wonderfully from the top of the hill to the bottom. It feels thousands of years old. M. was quiet and friendly. We met Don Vincenzo, he who has the care of the land and crops, coming slowly, slowly uphill in his black cassock, treading slowly in his great thick boots. He was reading a little book. He saluted us as we passed. Lower down a strapping girl was watching three merino sheep among the bushes. One sheep came on its exquisite slender legs to smell of me, with that insatiable curiosity of a *pecora*. Her nose was silken and elegant as she reached it to sniff at me, and the yearning, wondering, inquisitive look in her eyes made me realize that the Lamb of God must have been such a sheep as this.

M. was miserable at my going. Not so much at my going, as at being left alone up there. We came to the foot of the hill, on to the town highroad. So we went into a little cave of a wine-kitchen to drink a glass of wine. M. chatted a little with the young woman. He chatted with everybody. She eyed us closely, and asked if we were from the monastery. We said we were. She seemed to have a little lurking antagonism round her nose, at the mention of the monastery. M. paid for the wine—a franc. So we went out on the highroad, to part.

"Look," I said. "I can only give you twenty lire, because I shall need the rest for the journey——"

But he wouldn't take them. He looked at me wistfully. Then I went on down to the station, he turned away uphill. It was market in the town, and there were clusters of bullocks, and women cooking a little meal at a brazier under the trees, and goods spread out on the floor to sell, and sacks of beans and corn standing open, clustered round the trunks of the mulberry trees, and wagons with their shafts on the ground. The old peasants in their brown home-spun frieze and skin sandals were watching for the world. And there again was the Middle Ages.

It began to rain, however. Suddenly it began to pour with rain, and my coat was wet through, and my trouser-legs. The train from Rome was late—

I hoped not very late, or I should miss the boat. She came at last, and was full. I had to stand in the corridor. Then the man came to say dinner was served, so I luckily got a place and had my meal too. Sitting there in the dining-car, among the fat Neapolitans eating their macaroni, with the big glass windows steamed opaque and the rain beating outside, I let myself be carried away, away from the monastery, away from M., away from everything.

At Naples there was a bit of sunshine again, and I had time to go on foot to the Immacolatella, where the little steamer lay. There on the steamer I sat in a bit of sunshine, and felt that again the world had come to an end for me, and again my heart was broken. The steamer seemed to be making its way away from the old world, that had come to another end in me.

It was after this I decided to go to Sicily. In February, only a few days after my return from the monastery, I was on the steamer for Palermo, and at dawn looking out on the wonderful coast of Sicily. Sicily, tall, forever rising to her gem-like summits, all golden in dawn, and always glamorous, always hovering as if inaccessible, and yet so near, so distinct. Sicily, unknown to me, and amethystine-glamorous in the Mediterranean dawn: like the dawn of our day, the wonder-morning of our epoch.

I had various letters from M. He had told me to go to Girgenti. But I arrived in Girgenti when there was a strike of sulphur-miners, and they threw stones. So I did not want to live in Girgenti. M. hated Taormina—he had been everywhere, tried everywhere, and was not, I found, in any good odour in most places. He wrote, however, saying he hoped I would like it. And later he sent the Legion manuscript. I thought it was good, and told him so. It was offered to publishers in London, but rejected.

In early April I went with my wife to Syracuse for a few days: lovely, lovely days, with the purple anemones blowing in the Sicilian fields, and Adonis-blood red on the little ledges, and the corn rising

strong and green in the magical, malarial places, and
Etna flowing now to the northward, still with her
crown of snow. The lovely, lovely journey from Catania to Syracuse, in spring, winding round the
blueness of that sea, where the tall pink asphodel was
dying, and the yellow asphodel like a lily showing her
silk. Lovely, lovely Sicily, the dawnplace, Europe's
dawn, with Odysseus pushing his ship out of the
shadows into the blue. Whatever had died for me,
Sicily had then not died; dawn-lovely Sicily, and the
Ionian Sea.

We came back, and the world was lovely: our own
house above the almond trees, and the sea in the cove
below. Calabria glimmering like a changing opal
away to the left, across the blue, bright straits, and
all the great blueness of the lovely dawn-sea in
front, where the sun rose with a splendour like
trumpets every morning, and me rejoicing like a
madness in this dawn, day-dawn, life-dawn, the dawn
which is Greece, which is me.

Well, into this lyricism suddenly crept the serpent.
It was a lovely morning, still early. I heard a noise on
the stairs from the lower terrace, and went to look.
M. on the stairs, looking up at me with a frightened
face.

"Why!" I said. "Is it you?"

"Yes," he replied. "A terrible thing has happened."

He waited on the stairs, and I went down. Rather
unwillingly, because I detest terrible things, and
the people to whom they happen. So we leaned on the
creeper-covered rail of the terrace, under festoons
of creamy bignonia flowers, and looked at the pale
blue, ethereal sea.

"What terrible thing!" said I.

"When did you get back?" said he.

"Last evening."

"Oh! I came before. The *contadini* said they
thought you would come yesterday evening. I've been
here several days."

"Where are you staying?"

"At the San Domenico."

The San Domenico being then the most expensive hotel here, I thought he must have money. But I knew he wanted something of me.

"And are you staying some time?"

He paused a moment, and looked round cautiously.

"Is your wife there?" he asked, sotto voce.

"Yes, she's upstairs."

"Is there anyone who can hear?"

"No—only old Grazia down below, and she can't understand anyhow."

"Well," he said, stammering. "Let me tell you what's happened. I had to escape from the monastery. Don Bernardo had a telephone message from the town below, that the carabinieri were looking for an Americano—my name—Of course you can guess how I felt, up there! Awful! Well—! I had to fly at a moment's notice. I just put two shirts in a handbag and went. I slipped down a path—or rather, it isn't a path—down the back of the hill. Ten minutes after Don Bernardo had the message I was running down the hill."

"But what did they want you for?" I asked dismayed.

"Well," he faltered. "I told you about the cheque at Anzio, didn't I? Well, it seems the hotel people applied to the police. Anyhow," he added hastily, "I couldn't let myself be arrested up there, could I? So awful for the monastery!"

"Did they know then that you were in trouble?" I asked.

"Don Bernardo knew I had no money," he said. "Of course he had to know. Yes—he knew I was in *difficulty*. But, of course, he didn't know—well—*everything*." He laughed a little, comical laugh over the *everything*, as if he was just a little bit naughtily proud of it: most ruefully also.

"No," he continued, "that's what I'm most afraid of—that they'll find out everything at the monastery. Of course it's *dreadful*—the Americano, been staying there for months, and everything so nice and—well, you know how they are, they imagine every American is a millionaire, if not a multimillionaire. And sud-

denly to be wanted by the police! Of course it's
dreadful! Anything rather than a scandal at the
monastery—anything. Oh, how awful it was! I can
tell you, in that quarter of an hour, I sweated blood.
Don Bernardo lent me two hundred lire of the monastery money—which he'd no business to do. And I
escaped down the back of the hill, I walked to the
next station up the line, and took the next train—
the slow train—a few stations up towards Rome.
And there I changed and caught the *diretto* for
Sicily. I came straight to you—Of course I was in
agony: imagine it! I spent most of the time as far
as Naples in the lavatory." He laughed his little jerky
laugh.

"What class did you travel?"

"Second. All through the night. I arrived more
dead than alive, not having had a meal for two days—
only some sandwich stuff I bought on the platform."

"When did you come then?"

"I arrived on Saturday evening. I came out here on
Sunday morning, and they told me you were away.
Of course, imagine what it's like! I'm in torture
every minute, in torture, of course. Why, just imagine!" And he laughed his little laugh.

"But how much money have you got?"

"Oh—I've just got twenty-five francs and five
soldi." He laughed as if it was rather a naughty joke.

"But," I said, "If you've got no money, why do you
go to the San Domenico? How much do you pay
there?"

"Fifty lire a day. Of course it's *ruinous*——"

"But at the Bristol you only pay twenty-five—and
at Fichera's only twenty."

"Yes, I know you do," he said. "But I stayed at
the Bristol once, and I loathed the place. Such an
offensive manager. And I couldn't touch the food at
Fichera's."

"But who's going to pay for the San Domenico,
then?" I asked.

"Well, I thought," he said, "you know all those
manuscripts of mine? Well, you think they're some
good, don't you? Well, I thought if I made them over

to you, and you did what you could with them and just kept me going till I can get a new start—or till I can get away——"

I looked across the sea: the lovely morning-blue sea towards Greece.

"Where do you want to get away to?" I said.

"To Egypt. I know a man in Alexandria who owns newspapers there. I'm sure if I could get over there he'd give me an editorship or something. And of course money will come. I've written to ——, who was my *greatest friend,* in London. He will send me something——"

"And what else do you expect?"

"Oh, my article on the monastery was accepted by *Land and Water*—thanks to you and your kindness, of course. I thought if I might stay very quietly with you, for a time, and write some things I'm wanting to do, and collect a little money—and then get away to Egypt——"

He looked up into my face, as if he were trying all he could on me. First thing I knew was that I could not have him in the house with me; and even if I could have done it, my wife never could.

"You've got a lovely place here, perfectly beautiful," he said. "Of course, if it had to be Taormina, you've chosen far the best place here. I like this side so much better than the Etna side. Etna always there and people raving about it gets on my nerves. And a *charming* house, *charming.*"

He looked round the loggia and along the other terrace.

"Is it all yours?" he said.

"We don't use the ground floor. Come in here."

So we went into the *salotta.*

"Oh, what a beautiful room," he cried. "But perfectly palatial. Charming! Charming! *Much* the nicest house in Taormina."

"No," I said, "as a house it isn't very grand, though I like it for myself. It's just what I want. And I love the situation. But I'll go and tell my wife you are here."

"Will you?" he said, bridling nervously. "Of course

I've never met your wife." And he laughed the nervous, naughty, joky little laugh.

I left him, and ran upstairs to the kitchen. There was my wife, with wide eyes. She had been listening to catch the conversation. But M.'s voice was too hushed.

"M.!" said I softly. "The carabinieri wanted to arrest him at the monastery, so he has escaped here, and wants me to be responsible for him."

"Arrest him, what for?"

"Debts, I suppose. Will you come down and speak to him?"

M. of course was very charming with my wife. He kissed her hand humbly, in the correct German fashion, and spoke with an air of reverence that infallibly gets a woman.

"Such a beautiful place you have here," he said, glancing through the open doors of the room, at the sea beyond. "So clever of you to find it."

"Lawrence found it," said she. "Well, and you are in all kinds of difficulty!"

"Yes, isn't it terrible!" he said, laughing as if it were a joke—rather a wry joke. "I felt dreadful at the monastery. So dreadful for them, if there was any sort of scandal. And after I'd been so well received there—and so much the Signor Americano—Dreadful, don't you think?" He laughed again, like a naughty boy.

We had an engagement to lunch that morning. My wife was dressed, so I went to get ready. Then we told M. we must go out, and he accompanied us to the village. I gave him just the hundred francs I had in my pocket, and he said, could he come and see me that evening? I asked him to come next morning.

"You're so awfully kind," he said, simpering a little.

But by this time I wasn't feeling kind.

"He's quite nice," said my wife. "But he's rather an impossible little person. And you'll see, he'll be a nuisance. Whatever do you pick up such dreadful people for?"

"Nay," I said. "You can't accuse me of picking up dreadful people. He's the first. And even he isn't dreadful."

The next morning came a letter from Don Bernardo addressed to me, but only enclosing a letter to M. So he was using my address. At ten o'clock he punctually appeared, slipping in as if to avoid notice. My wife would not see him, so I took him out on the terrace again.

"Isn't it beautiful here!" he said. "Oh, so beautiful! If only I had my peace of mind. Of course I sweat blood every time anybody comes through the door. You are splendidly private out here."

"Yes," I said. "But, M., there isn't a room for you in the house. There isn't a spare room anyway. You'd better think of getting something cheaper in the village."

"But what can I get?" he snapped.

That rather took my breath away. Myself, I had never been near the San Domenico Hotel. I knew I simply could not afford it.

"What made you go to the San Domenico in the first place?" I said. "The most expensive hotel in the place!"

"Oh, I'd stayed there for two months, and they knew me, and I knew they'd ask no questions. I knew they wouldn't ask for a deposit or anything."

"But nobody dreams of asking for a deposit," I said.

"Anyhow, I shan't take my meals there. I shall just take coffee in the morning. I've had to eat there so far, because I was starved to death, and had no money to go out. But I had two meals in that little restaurant yesterday; disgusting food."

"And how much did that cost?"

"Oh, fourteen francs and fifteen francs, with a quarter of wine—and such a poor meal!"

Now I was annoyed, knowing that I myself should have bought bread and cheese for one franc, and eaten it in my room. But also I realized that the modern creed says, if you sponge, sponge thor-

oughly; and also that every man has a "right to
live," and that if he can manage to live well, no
matter at whose expense, all credit to him. This is
the kind of talk one accepts in one's slipshod moments; now it was actually tried on me, I didn't like
it at all.

"But who's going to pay your bill at the San
Domenico?" I said.

"I thought you'd advance me the money on those
manuscripts."

"It's no good talking about the money on the manuscripts," I said. "I should have to give it to you. And
as a matter of fact, I've got just sixty pounds in the
bank in England, and about fifteen hundred lire here.
My wife and I have got to live on that. We don't
spend as much in a week as you spend in three days
at the San Domenico. It's no good your thinking I
can advance money on the manuscripts. I can't. If I
was rich, I'd give you money. But I've got no money,
and never have had any. Have you nobody you can
go to?"

"I'm waiting to hear from ———. When I go back
into the village, I'll telegraph to him," replied M., a
little crestfallen. "Of course I'm in torture night and
day, or I wouldn't appeal to you like this. I know it's
unpleasant for you"—he put his hand on my arm
and looked up beseechingly—"but what am I to do?"

"You must get out of the San Domenico," I said.
"That's the first thing."

"Yes," he said, a little piqued now. "I know it is.
I'm going to ask Pancrazio Melenga to let me have
a room in his house. He knows me quite well—he's
an awfully nice fellow. He'll do *anything* for me—
anything. I was just going there yesterday afternoon when you were coming from Timeo. He was
out, so I left word with his wife, who is a charming
little person. If he has a room to spare, I know he
will let me have it. And he's a *splendid* cook—splendid. By far the nicest food in Taormina."

"Well," I said. "If you settle with Melenga, I will
pay your bill at the San Domenico, but I can't do
any more. I simply can't."

"But what am I to *do?*" he snapped.

"I don't know," I said. "You must think."

"I came here," he said, "thinking you would help me. What am I to do, if you won't? I shouldn't have come to Taormina at all, save for you. Don't be unkind to me—don't speak so coldly to me." He put his hand on my arm, and looked up at me with tears swimming in his eyes. Then he turned aside his face, overcome with tears. I looked away at the Ionian Sea, feeling my blood turn to ice and the sea go black. I loathe scenes such as this.

"Did you telegraph to ——?" I said.

"Yes. I have no answer yet. I hope you don't mind —I gave your address for a reply."

"Oh," I said. "There's a letter for you from Don Bernardo."

He went pale. I was angry at his having used my address in this manner.

"Nothing further has happened at the monastery," he said. "They rang up from the *questura,* from the police station, and Don Bernardo answered that the Americano had left for Rome. Of course I did take the train for Rome. And Don Bernardo wanted me to go to Rome. He advised me to do so. I didn't tell him I was here till I had got here. He thought I should have had more resources in Rome, and of course I should. I should certainly have gone there, if it hadn't been for *you here*——"

Well, I was getting tired and angry. I would not give him any more money at the moment. I promised if he would leave the hotel I would pay his bill, but he must leave it at once. He went off to settle with Melenga. He asked again if he could come in the afternoon. I said I was going out.

He came, nevertheless, while I was out. This time my wife found him on the stairs. She was for hating him, of course. So she stood immovable on the top stair, and he stood two stairs lower, and he kissed her hand in utter humility. And he pleaded with her, and as he looked up to her on the stairs the tears ran down his face and he trembled with distress. And her spine crept up and down with distaste and discomfort. But he broke into a few phrases of touching German, and I know he broke down her reserve and she promised him all he wanted. This part she would never confess, though. Only she was shivering with revulsion and excitement and even a sense of power, when I came home.

That was why M. appeared more impertinent than ever, next morning. He had arranged to go to Melenga's house the following day, and to pay ten francs a day for his room, his meals extra. So that was something. He made a long tale about not eating any of his meals in the hotel now, but pretending he was invited out, and eating in the little restaurants where the food was so bad. And he had now only fifteen lire left in his pocket. But I was cold, and wouldn't give him any more. I said I would give him money next day, for his bill.

He had now another request, and a new tone.

"Won't you do *one more* thing for me?" he said. "Oh, do! Do do this one thing for me. I want you to go to the monastery and bring away my important papers and some clothes and my important trinkets. I have made a list of the things here—and where you'll find them in my writing-table and in the chest of drawers. I don't think you'll have any trouble. Don Bernardo has the keys. He will open everything for you. And I beg you, *in the name of God*, don't let anybody else see the things. Not even Don Bernardo. Don't, whatever you do, let him see the papers and manuscripts you are bringing. If he sees them, there's an end to me at the monastery. I can *never* go back there. I am ruined in their eyes for ever. As it is, although Don Bernardo is the best person in the world and my dearest friend, still—you know what people are, especially monks. A little curious, don't you know, a little inquisitive. Well, let us hope for the best as far as that goes. But you will do this for me, won't you? I shall be so eternally grateful."

Now a journey to the monastery meant a terrible twenty hours in the train each way—all that awful journey through Calabria to Naples and northwards It meant mixing myself up in this man's affairs. I meant appearing as his accomplice at the monastery. It meant travelling with all his "compromising" papers and his valuables. And all this time, I never knew what mischiefs he had really been up to, and I didn't trust him, not for one single second. He would tell me nothing save that Anzio hotel cheque. I knew that wasn't all, by any means. So I mistrusted him. And with a feeling of utter mistrust goes a feeling of contempt and dislike— And finally, it would have cost me at least ten pounds sterling, which I simply did not want to spend in waste.

"I don't want to do that," I said.

"Why not? he asked, sharp, looking green. He had planned it all out.

"No, I don't want to."

"Oh, but I *can't* remain here as I am. I've got no *clothes*—I've got nothing to *wear*. I *must* have my things from the monastery. What can I do? What can I do? I came to you, if it hadn't been for you I should have gone to Rome. I came to you— Oh, yes, you *will* go. You *will* go, won't you? You *will* go to the monastery for my things?" And again he put his hand on my arm, and the tears began to fall from his upturned eyes. I turned my head aside. Never had the Ionian Sea looked so sickening to me.

"I don't *want* to," said I.

"But you *will!* You will! You *will* go to the monastery for me, won't you? Everything else is no good if you won't. I've got nothing to wear. I haven't got my manuscripts to work on, I can't do the things I am doing. Here I live in a sweat of anxiety. I try to work, and I can't settle. I can't do anything. It's dreadful. I shan't have a minute's peace till I have got those things from the monastery, till I know they can't get at my private papers. You will do this for me! You will, won't you? Please do! Oh, please do!" And again tears.

And I with my bowels full of bitterness, loathing the thought of that journey there and back, on such an errand. Yet not quite sure that I ought to refuse. And he pleaded and struggled, and tried to bully me with tears and entreaty and reproach, to do his will.

And I couldn't quite refuse. But neither could I agree.

At last I said:

"I don't want to go, and I tell you. I won't promise to go. And I won't say that I will not go. I won't say until tomorrow. Tomorrow I will tell you. Don't come to the house. I will be in the Corso at ten o'clock."

"I didn't doubt for a minute you would do this for me," he said. "Otherwise I should never have come to Taormina." As if he had done me an honour in coming to Taormina; and as if I had betrayed *him*.

"Well," I said. "If you make these messes you'll have to get out of them yourself. I don't know why you are *in* such a mess."

"Any man may make a mistake," he said sharply, as if correcting me.

"Yes, a *mistake!*" said I. "If it's a question of a mistake."

So once more he went, humbly, beseechingly, and yet, one could not help but feel, with all that terrible insolence of the humble. It is the humble, the wistful, the would-be loving souls today who bully us with their charity-demanding insolence. They just make up their minds, these needful sympathetic souls, that one is there to do their will. Very good.

I decided in the day I would *not* go. Without reasoning it out, I knew I *really* didn't want to go. I plainly didn't want it. So I wouldn't go.

The morning came again hot and lovely. I set off to the village. But there was M. watching for me on the path beyond the valley. He came forward and took my hand warmly, clingingly. I turned back, to remain in the country. We talked for a minute of his leaving the hotel—he was going that afternoon, he had asked for his bill. But he was waiting for the other answer.

"And I have decided," I said, "I won't go to the monastery."

"You won't." He looked at me. I saw how yellow he was round the eyes, and yellow under his reddish skin.

"No," I said.

And it was final. He knew it. We went some way in silence. I turned in at the garden gate. It was a lovely, lovely morning of hot sun. Butterflies were flapping over the rosemary hedges and over a few little red poppies, the young vines smelt sweet in flower, very sweet, the corn was tall and green, and there were still some wild, rose-red gladiolus flowers among the watery green of the wheat. M. had accepted my refusal. I expected him to be angry. But no, he seemed quieter, wistfuller, and he seemed almost to love me for having refused him. I stood at a bend in the path. The sea was heavenly blue, rising up beyond the vines and olive leaves, lustrous pale lacquer blue as only the Ionian Sea can be. Away at the brook below the women were washing, and one could hear the chock-chock-chock of linen beating against the stones. I felt M. then an intolerable weight and like a clot of dirt over everything.

"May I come in?" he said to me.

"No," I said. "Don't come to the house. My wife doesn't want it."

Even that he accepted without any offence, and seemed only to like me better for it. That was a puzzle to me. I told him I would leave a letter and a cheque for him at the bank in the Corso that afternoon.

I did so, writing a cheque for a few pounds, enough to cover his bill and leave a hundred lire or so over, and a letter to say I could *not* do any more, and I didn't want to see him any more.

So, there was an end of it for a moment. Yet I felt him looming in the village, waiting. I had rashly said I would go to tea with him to the villa of one of the Englishmen resident here, whose acquaintance I had not made. Alas, M. kept me to the promise. As I came home he appealed to me again. He was rather insolent. What good to him, he said, were the few pounds I had given him? He had a hundred and fifty lire left. What good was that? I realized it really was not a solution, and said nothing. Then he spoke of his plans for getting to Egypt. The fare, he had found out, was thirty-five pounds. And where were thirty-five pounds coming from? Not from me.

I spent a week avoiding him, wondering what on earth the poor devil was doing, and yet *determined* he should not be a parasite on me. If I could have given him fifty pounds and sent him to Egypt to be a parasite on somebody else, I would have done so. Which is what we call charity. However, I couldn't.

My wife chafed, crying: "What have you done! We shall have him on our hands all our life. We can't let him starve. It is degrading, degrading, to have him hanging on to us."

"Yes," I said. "He must starve or work or something. I am not God who is responsible for him."

M. was determined not to lose his status as a gentleman. In a way I sympathized with him. He would never be out at elbows. That is your modern rogue. He will not degenerate outwardly. Certain standards of a gentleman he *would* keep up: he would be well-dressed, he would be lavish with borrowed money, he would be as far as possible honourable in his small transactions of daily life. Well, very good. I sympathized with him to a certain degree. If he could find his own way out, well and good. Myself, I was not his way out.

Ten days passed. It was hot and I was going about the terrace in pyjamas and a big old straw hat, when, suddenly, a Sicilian, handsome, in the prime of life, and in his best black suit, smiling at me and taking off his hat!

And could he speak to me? I threw away my straw hat, and we went into the *salotta*. He handed me a note.

"*Il Signor M. mi ha data questa lettera per Lei!*" he began, and I knew what was coming. Melenga had been a waiter in good hotels, had saved money, built himself a fine house which he let to foreigners. He was a pleasant fellow, and at his best now, because he was in a rage. I must repeat M.'s letter from memory: "Dear Lawrence, would you do me another kindness? *Land and Water* sent a cheque for seven guineas for the article on the monastery, and Don

Bernardo forwarded this to me under Melenga's name. But unfortunately he made a mistake, and put Orazio instead of Pancrazio, so the postoffice would not deliver the letter, and have returned it to the monastery. This morning Melenga insulted me, and I cannot stay in his house another minute. Will you be so kind as to advance me these seven guineas? I shall leave Taormina at once, for Malta."

I asked Melenga what had happened, and read him the letter. He was handsome in his rage, lifting his brows and suddenly smiling.

"*Ma senta, signore!* Signor M. has been in my house for ten days, and lived well, and eaten well, and drunk well, and I have not seen a single penny of his money. I go out in the morning and buy all the things, all he wants, and my wife cooks it, and he is very pleased, very pleased, has never eaten such good food in his life, and everything is splendid, splendid. And he never pays a penny. Not a penny. Says he is waiting for money from England, from America, from India. But the money never comes. And I am a poor man, signore, I have a wife and child to keep. I have already spent three hundred lira for this Signor M., and I never see a penny of it back. And he says the money is coming, it is coming. But when? He never says he has got no money. He says he is expecting. Tomorrow—always tomorrow. It will come tonight, it will come tomorrow. This makes me in a rage. Till at last this morning I said to him I would bring nothing in, and he shouldn't have not so much as a drop of coffee in my house until he paid for it. It displeases me, signore, to say such a thing. I have known Signor M. for many years, and he has always had money, and always been pleasant, *molto bravo*, and also generous with his money. *Si, lo so!* And my wife, *poverina,* she cries and says if the man has no money he must eat. But he doesn't say he has no money. He says always it is coming, it is coming, today, tomorrow, today, tomorrow. *E non viene mai niente.* And this enrages me, signore. So I said that to him this morning. And he said he wouldn't stay in my house, and that I had

insulted him, and he sends me this letter to you,
signore, and says you will send him the money. *Ecco
come!*"

Between his rage he smiled at me. One thing,
however, I could see: he was not going to lose his
money, M. or no M.

"Is it true that a letter came which the post would
not deliver?" I asked him.

"Si, signore, è vero. It came yesterday, addressed
to me. And why, signore, why do his letters come
addressed in my name? Why? Unless he has done
something—?"

He looked at me inquiringly. I felt already mixed
up in shady affairs.

"Yes," I said, "there is something. But I don't
know exactly what. I don't ask, because I don't want
to know in these affairs. It is better not to know."

"Già! Già! Molto meglio, signore. There will be
something. There will be something happened that
he had to escape from that monastery. And it will
be some affair of the police."

"Yes, I think so," said I. "Money and the police.
Probably debts. I don't ask. He is only an acquaintance of mine, not a friend."

"Sure it will be an affair of the police," he said
with a grimace. "If not, why does he use my name!
Why don't his letters come in his own name? Do you
believe, signore, that he has any money? Do you
think this money will come?"

"I'm sure he's *got* no money," I said. "Whether
anybody will send him any, I don't know."

The man watched me attentively.

"He's got nothing?" he said.

"No. At present he's got nothing."

Then Pancrazio exploded on the sofa.

"Allora! Well, then! Well, then, why does he come
to my house, why does he come and take a room in my
house, and ask me to buy food, good food as for a
gentleman who can pay, and a flask of wine, and
everything, if he has no money? If he has no money,
why does he come to Taormina? It is many years that

he has been in Italy—ten years, fifteen years. And he has no money. Where has he had his money from before? Where?"

"From his writing, I suppose."

"Well, then why doesn't he get money for his writing now? He writes. He writes, he works, he says it is for the big newspapers."

"It is difficult to sell things."

"Heh! Then why doesn't he live on what he made before? He hasn't a soldo. He hasn't a penny—But how! How did he pay his bill at the San Domenico?"

"I had to lend him money for that. He really hadn't a penny."

"You! You! Well, then, he has been in Italy all these years. How is it he has nobody that he can ask for a hundred lire or two? Why does he come to you? Why? Why has he nobody in Rome, in Florence, anywhere?"

"I wonder that myself."

"Sicuro! He's been all these years here. And why doesn't he speak proper Italian? After all these years, and speaks all upside-down, it isn't Italian, an ugly confusion. Why? Why? He passes for a signore, for a man of education. And he comes to take the bread out of my mouth. And I have a wife and child, I am a poor man, I have nothing to eat myself if everything goes to a mezzo-signore like him. Nothing! He owes me now three hundred lire. But he will not leave my house, he will not leave Taormina till he has paid. I will go to the *prefettura,* I will go to the *questura,* to the police. I will not be swindled by such a mezzo-signore. What does he want to do? If he has no money, what does he want to do?"

"To go to Egypt, where he says he can earn some," I replied briefly. But I was feeling bitter in the mouth. When the man called M. a mezzo-signore, a half-gentleman, it was so true. And at the same time it was so cruel, and so rude. And Melenga—there I sat in my pyjamas and sandals—probably he would be calling me also a mezzo-signore, or a quarto-signore even. He was a Sicilian who feels he is being done out of his money—and that is saying everything.

"To Egypt! And who will pay for him to go? Who will give him money? But he must pay me first. He must pay me first."

"He says," I said, "that in the letter which went back to the monastery there was a cheque for seven pounds—some six hundred lire—and he asks me to send him this money, and when the letter is returned again I shall have the cheque that is in it."

Melenga watched me.

"Six hundred lire—" he said.

"Yes."

"Oh, well, then. If he pays me, he can stay—" he said; he almost added: "till the six hundred is finished." But he left it unspoken.

"But am I going to send the money? Am I sure that what he says is true?"

"I think it is true. I think it is true," said he. "The letter *did* come."

I thought for a while.

"First," I said, "I will write and ask him if it is quite true, and to give me a guarantee."

"Very well," said Melenga.

I wrote to M., saying that if he could assure me that what he said about the seven guineas was quite correct, and if he would give me a note to the editor of *Land and Water,* saying that the cheque was to be paid to me, I would send the seven guineas.

Melenga was back in another half-hour. He brought a note which began:

"Dear Lawrence, I seem to be living in an atmosphere of suspicion. First Melenga this morning, and now you—" Those are the exact opening words. He went on to say that of course his word was true, and he enclosed a note to the editor, saying the seven guineas were to be transferred to me. He asked me please to send the money, as he could not stay another night at Melenga's house, but would leave for Catania, where, by the sale of some trinkets, he hoped to make some money and to see once more about a passage to Egypt. He had been to Catania once already—travelling *third class!*—but had failed to find any cargo boat that would take him to Alexandria. He would get away now to Malta. His things were being sent down to Syracuse from the monastery.

I wrote and said I hoped he would get safely away, and enclosed the cheque.

"This will be for six hundred lire," said Melenga.

"Yes," said I.

"*Eh, va bene!* If he pays the three hundred lire, he can stop in my house for thirty lire a day."

"He says he won't sleep in your house again."

"*Ma!* Let us see. If he likes to stay. He has always been a *bravo signore*. I have always liked him quite well. If he wishes to stay and pay me thirty lire a day——"

The man smiled at me rather greenly.

"I'm afraid he is offended," said I.

"*Eh, va bene! Ma senta, signore.* When he was here before—you know I have this house of mine to let. And you know the English signorina goes away in the summer. Oh, very well. Says M., he writes for a newspaper, he owns a newspaper, I don't know what, in Rome. He will put in an advertisement advertising my villa. And so I shall get somebody to take it. Very well. And he put in the advertisement. He sent me the paper and I saw it there. But no one came to take my villa. *Va bene!* But after a year, in the January, that is, came a bill for me for twenty-two lire to pay for it. Yes, I had to pay the twenty-two lire, for nothing—for the advertisement which Signor M. put in the paper."

"Bah!" said I.

He shook hands with me and left. The next day he came after me in the street, and said that M. had departed the previous evening for Catania. As a matter of fact the post brought me a note of thanks from Catania. M. was never indecent, and one could never dismiss him just as a scoundrel. He was not. He was one of these modern parasites who just assume their right to live and live well, leaving the

payment to anybody who can, will, or must pay. The
end is inevitably swindling.

There came also a letter from Rome, addressed to
me. I opened it unthinking. It was for M., from an
Italian lawyer, stating that inquiry had been made
about the writ against M., and that it was for *qualche
affare di truffa,* some affair of swindling: that the
lawyer had seen this, that, and the other person, but
nothing could be done. He regretted, etc., etc. I forwarded this letter to M. at Syracuse, and hoped to
God it was ended. Ah, I breathed free now he had
gone.

But, no. A friend who was with us dearly wanted
to go to Malta. It is only about eighteen hours'
journey from Taormina—easier than going to
Naples. So our friend invited us to take the trip with
her, as her guests. This was rather jolly. I calculated that M., who had been gone a week or so,
would easily have got to Malta. I had had a friendly
letter from him from Syracuse, thanking me for the
one I had forwarded, and enclosing an I.O.U. for
the various sums of money he had had.

So, on a hot, hot Thursday, we were sitting in the
train again running south, the four and a half hours'
journey to Syracuse. And M. dwindled now into the
past. If we should see him! But no, it was impossible.
After all the wretchedness of that affair we were in
holiday spirits.

The train ran into Syracuse station. We sat on, to
go the few yards further into the port. A tout
climbed on the foot-board: Were we going to Malta?
Well, we couldn't. There was a strike of the steamers,
we couldn't go. When would the steamer go? Who
knows? Perhaps tomorrow.

We got down crestfallen. What should we do?
There stood the express train about to start off
back northwards. We could be home again that
evening. But, no, it would be too much of a fiasco.
We let the train go, and trailed off into the town,
to the Grand Hotel, which is an old Italian place
just opposite the port. It is rather a dreary hotel—

and many bloodstains of squashed mosquitoes on the bedroom walls. Ah, vile mosquitoes!

However, nothing to be done. Syracuse port is fascinating too, a tiny port with the little Sicilian ships having the slanting eyes painted on the prow, to see the way, and a coal boat from Cardiff, and one American and two Scandinavian steamers—no more. But there were two torpedo boats in the harbour, and it was like a *festa*, a strange, lousy *festa*.

Beautiful the round harbour where the Athenian ships came. And wonderful, beyond, the long sinuous sky-line of the long flat-topped table-land hills which run along the southern coast, so different from the peaky, pointed, bunched effect of many-tipped Sicily in the north. The sun went down behind that lovely, sinuous sky-line, the harbour water was gold and red, the people promenaded in thick streams under the pomegranate trees and hibiscus trees. Arabs in white burnouses and fat Turks in red fezzes and black alpaca long coats strolled also—waiting for the steamer.

Next day it was very hot. We went to the consul and the steamer agency. There was real hope that the brute of a steamer might actually sail that night. So we stayed on, and wandered round the town on the island, the old solid town, and sat in the church looking at the grand Greek columns embedded there in the walls.

When I came in to lunch, the porter said there was a letter for me. Impossible! said I. But he brought me a note. Yes. M.! He was staying at the other hotel along the front. "Dear Lawrence, I saw you this morning, all three of you walking down the Via Nazionale, but you would not look at me. I have got my visés and everything ready. The strike of the steamboats has delayed me here. I am sweating blood. I have a last request to make of you. Can you let me have ninety lire, to make up what I need for my hotel bill? If I cannot have this I am lost. I hoped to find you at the hotel but the porter said you were out. I am at the Casa Politi, passing every half-hour in agony. If you can be so kind as to stretch your generosity to this last loan, of course I shall be eternally grateful. I can pay you back once I get to Malta——"

Well, here was a blow! The worst was that he thought I had cut him—a thing I wouldn't have done. So after luncheon behold me going through the terrific sun of that harbour front of Syracuse, an enormous and powerful sun, to the Casa Politi. The porter recognized me and looked inquiringly. M. was out, and I said I would call again at four o'clock.

It happened we were in the town eating ices at four, so I didn't get to his hotel till half-past. He was out—gone to look for me. So I left a note saying I had not seen him in the Via Nazionale, that I had called twice, and that I should be in the Grand Hotel in the evening.

When we came in at seven, M. in the hall, sitting, the picture of misery and endurance. He took my hand in both his, and bowed to the women, who nodded and went upstairs. He and I went and sat in the empty lounge. Then he told me the trials he had had—how his luggage had come, and the station had charged him eighteen lire a day for deposit; how he had had to wait on at the hotel because of the ship; how he had tried to sell his trinkets, and had today parted with his opal sleevelinks—so that now he only wanted seventy, not ninety lire. I gave him a hundred note, and he looked into my eyes, his own eyes swimming with tears, and he said he was sweating blood.

Well, the steamer went that night. She was due to leave at ten. We went on board after dinner. We were going second class. And so, for once, was M. It was only an eight hours' crossing, yet, in spite of all the blood he had sweated, he would not go third class. In a way I admired him for sticking to his principles. I should have gone third myself, out of shame of spending somebody else's money. He would not give way to such weakness. He knew that as far as the world goes, you're a first-class gentleman if you have a first-class ticket; if you have a third, no gentleman at all. It behoved him to be a gentleman. I understood his point, but the women were indignant. And I was just rather tired of him and his gentlemanliness.

It amused me very much to lean on the rail of the upper deck and watch the people coming on board —first going into the little customs house with their baggage, then scuffling up the gangway on board. The tall Arabs in their ghostly white woollen robes came carrying their sacks: they were going on to Tripoli. The fat Turk in his fez and long black alpaca coat with white drawers underneath came beaming up to the second class. There was a great row in the customs house; and then, simply running like a beetle with rage, there came on board a little Maltese or Greek fellow, followed by a tall lantern-jawed fellow, both seedy-looking scoundrels suckled in scoundrelism. They raved and nearly threw their arms away into the sea, talking wildly in some weird language with the fat Turk, who listened solemnly, away below on the deck. They then rushed to somebody else. Of course, we were dying with curiosity. Thank heaven I heard men talking in Italian. It appears the two seedy fellows were trying to smuggle silver coin in small sacks and rolls out of the country. They were detected. But they declared they had a right to take it away, as it was foreign specie, English florins and half-crowns, and South American dollars and Spanish money. The customs officer, however, detained the lot. The little enraged beetle of a fellow ran back and forth from the ship to the customs, from the customs to the ship, afraid to go without his money, afraid the ship would go without him.

At five minutes to ten, there came M., very smart in his little grey overcoat and grey curly hat, walking very smart and erect and genteel, and followed by a porter with a barrow of luggage. They went into the customs, M. in his grey suède gloves passing rapidly and smartly in, like the grandest gentleman on earth, and with his grey suède hands throwing

open his luggage for inspection. From on board we
could see the interior of the little customs shed.

Yes, he was through. Brisk, smart, superb, like
the grandest little gentleman on earth, strutting because he was late, he crossed the bit of flagged pavement and came up the gangway, haughty as you
can wish. The carabinieri were lounging by the foot
of the gangway, fooling with one another. The little
gentleman passed them with his nose in the air,
came quickly on board, followed by his porter, and
in a moment disappeared. After about five minutes
the porter reappeared—a red-haired fellow, I knew
him—he even saluted me from below, the brute. But
M. lay in hiding.

I trembled for him at every unusual stir. There
on the quay stood the English consul with his bull-
dog, and various elegant young officers with yellow
on their uniforms, talking to elegant young Italian
ladies in black hats with stiff ospreys and bunchy
furs, and gangs of porters and hotel people and on-
lookers. Then came a tramp-tramp-tramp of a squad
of soldiers in red fezzes and baggy grey trousers.
Instead of coming on board they camped on the quay.
I wondered if all these had come for poor M. But
apparently not.

So the time passed, till nearly midnight, when one
of the elegant young lieutenants began to call the
names of the soldiers, and the soldiers answered,
and one after another filed on board with his kit. So,
they were on board, on their way to Africa.

Now somebody called out, and the visitors began
to leave the boat. Barefooted sailors and a boy ran
to raise the gangway. The last visitor or official with
a bunch of papers stepped off the gangway. People
on shore began to wave handkerchiefs. The red-
fezzed soldiers leaned like so many flower-pots over
the lower rail. There was a calling of farewells. The
ship was fading into the harbour, the people on shore
seemed smaller, under the lamp, in the deep night—
without one's knowing why.

So, we passed out of the harbour, passed the
glittering lights of Ortygia, past the two lighthouses,

into the open Mediterranean. The noise of a ship in
the open sea! It was a still night, with stars, only a
bit chill. And the ship churned through the water.

Suddenly, like a revenant, appeared M. near us,
leaning on the rail and looking back at the lights of
Syracuse sinking already forlorn and little on the
low darkness. I went to him.

"Well," he said, with his little smirk of a laugh.
"Good-bye, Italy!"

"Not a sad farewell either," said I.

"No, my word, not this time," he said. "But what
an awful long time we were starting! A *brutta
mezz'ora* for me, indeed. Oh, my word, I begin to
breathe free for the first time since I left the monastery! How awful it's been! But of course, in Malta, I
shall be all right. Don Bernardo has written to his
friends there. They'll have everything ready for me
that I want, and I can pay you back the money you
so kindly lent me."

We talked for some time, leaning on the inner rail
of the upper deck.

"Oh," he said, "there's Commander So-and-so, of
the British fleet. He's stationed in Malta. I made his
acquaintance in the hotel. I hope we're going to be
great friends in Malta. I hope I shall have an opportunity to introduce you to him. Well, I suppose
you will want to be joining your ladies. So long,
then. Oh, for tomorrow morning! I never longed so
hard to be in the British Empire—" He laughed, and
strutted away.

In a few minutes we three, leaning on the rail of
the second-class upper deck, saw our little friend
large as life on the first-class deck, smoking a cigar
and chatting in an absolutely first-class-ticket
manner with the above mentioned Commander. He
pointed us out to the Commander, and we felt the
first-class passengers were looking across at us
second-class passengers with pleasant interest. The
women went behind a canvas heap to laugh, I hid
my face under my hat-brim to grin and watch.
Larger than any first-class ticketer leaned our little
friend on the first-class rail, and whiffed at his cigar.

So *dégagé* and so genteel he could be. Only I noticed
he wilted a little when the officers of the ship came
near.

He was still on the first-class deck when we went
down to sleep. In the morning I came up soon after
dawn. It was a lovely summer Mediterranean morning, with the sun rising up in a gorgeous golden
rage, and the sea so blue, so fairy blue, as the Mediterranean is in summer. We were approaching quite
near to a rocky, pale yellow island with some vine-
yards, rising magical out of the swift blue sea into
the morning radiance. The rocks were almost as
pale as butter, the islands were like golden shadows
loitering in the midst of the Mediterranean, lonely
among all the blue.

M. came up to my side.

"Isn't it lovely! Isn't it beautiful!" he said. "I love
approaching these islands in the early morning." He
had almost recovered his assurance, and the slight
pomposity and patronizing tone I had first known in
him. "In two hours I shall be free! Imagine it! Oh,
what a beautiful feeling!" I looked at him in the
morning light. His face was a good deal broken by
his last month's experience, older looking, and
dragged. Now that the excitement was nearing its
end, the tiredness began to tell on him. He was yellowish round the eyes, and the whites of his round,
rather impudent blue eyes were discoloured.

Malta was drawing near. We saw the white fringe
of the sea upon the yellow rocks, and a white road
looping on the yellow rocky hillside. I thought of St.
Paul, who must have been blown this way, must have
struck the island from this side. Then we saw the
heaped glitter of the square facets of houses, Valletta, splendid above the Mediterranean, and a tangle
of shipping and dreadnoughts and watchtowers in
the beautiful, locked-in harbour.

We had to go down to have passports examined.
The officials sat in the long saloon. It was a horrible
squash and squeeze of the first- and second-class
passengers. M. was a little ahead of me. I saw the
American eagle on his passport. Yes, he passed all

right. Once more he was free. As he passed away he turned and gave a condescending affable nod to me and to the Commander, who was just behind me.

The ship was lying in Valletta harbour. I saw M., quite superb and brisk now, ordering a porter with his luggage into a boat. The great rocks rose above us, yellow and carved, cut straight by man. On top were all the houses. We got at last into a boat and were rowed ashore. Strange to be on British soil and to hear English. We got a carriage and drove up the steep highroad through the cutting in the rock, up to the town. There in the big square we had coffee, sitting out of doors. A military band went by, playing splendidly in the bright, hot morning. The Maltese lounged about, and watched. Splendid the band, and the soldiers! One felt the splendour of the British Empire, let the world say what it likes. But, alas, as one stayed on even in Malta, one felt the old lion had gone foolish and amiable. Foolish and amiable, with the weak amiability of old age.

We stayed in the Great Britain Hotel. Of course one could not be in Valletta for twenty-four hours without meeting M. There he was, in the Strada Reale, strutting in a smart white duck suit, with a white piqué cravat. But, alas, he had no white shoes: they had got lost or stolen. He had to wear black boots with his summer finery.

He was staying in an hotel a little further down our street, and he begged me to call and see him, he begged me to come to lunch. I promised and went. We went into his bedroom, and he rang for more sodas.

"How wonderful it is to be here!" he said brightly. "Don't you like it immensely? And, oh, how wonderful to have a whisky and soda. Well, now, say when."

He finished one bottle of Black and White, and opened another. The waiter, a good-looking Maltese fellow, appeared with two siphons. M. was very much the signore with him, and at the same time very familiar: as I should imagine a rich Roman of the merchant class might have been with a pet slave.

We had quite a nice lunch, and whisky and soda and a bottle of French wine. And M. was the charming and attentive host.

After lunch we talked again of manuscripts and publishers and how he might make money. I wrote one or two letters for him. He was anxious to get something under way. And yet the trouble of these arrangements was almost too much for his nerves. His face looked broken and old, but not like an old man's, like an old boy's, and he was really very irritable.

For my own part I was soon tired of Malta, and would gladly have left after three days. But there was the strike of steamers still, we had to wait on. M. professed to be enjoying himself hugely, making excursions every day, to St. Paul's Bay and to the other islands. He had also made various friends or acquaintances. Particularly two young men, Maltese, who were friends of Don Bernardo. He introduced me to these two young men: one Gabriel Mazzaiba and the other Salonia. They had small businesses down on the wharf. Salonia asked M. to go for a drive in a motor-car round the island, and M. pressed me to go too. Which I did. And swiftly, on a Saturday afternoon, we dodged about in the car upon that dreadful island, first to some fearful and stony bay, arid, treeless, desert, a bit of stony desert by the sea, with unhappy villas and a sordid, scrap-iron front; then away inland up long and dusty roads, across a bone-dry, bone-bare, hideous landscape. True, there was ripening corn, but this was all of a colour with the dust-yellow, bone-bare island. Malta is all a pale, softish, yellowish rock, just like Bath brick: this goes into fathomless dust. And the island is stark as a corpse, no trees, no bushes even: a fearful landscape, cultivated, and weary with ages of weariness, and old weary houses here and there.

We went to the old capital in the centre of the island, and this is interesting. The town stands on a bluff of hill in the middle of the dreariness, looking at Valletta in the distance, and the sea. The houses are all pale yellow, and tall, and silent, as if for-

saken. There is a cathedral, too, and a fortress out-
look over the sun-blazed, sun-dried, disheartening
island. Then we dashed off to another village and
climbed a church-dome that rises like a tall blister on
the plain, with houses round and corn beyond and
dust that has no glamour, stale, weary, like bone-
dust, and thorn hedges sometimes, and some tin-like
prickly pears. In the dusk we came round by St.
Paul's Bay, back to Valletta.

The young men were very pleasant, very patriotic
for Malta, very Catholic. We talked politics and a
thousand things. M. was gently patronizing, and
seemed, no doubt, to the two Maltese a very elegant
and travelled and wonderful gentleman. They, who
had never seen even a wood, thought how wonderful a forest must be, and M. talked to them of
Russia and of Germany.

But I was glad to leave that bone-dry, hideous
island. M. begged me to stay longer: but not for
worlds! He was establishing himself securely: was
learning the Maltese language, and cultivating a
thorough acquaintance with the island. And he was
going to establish himself. Mazzaiba was exceed-
ingly kind to him, helping him in every way. In
Rabato, the suburb of the old town—a quiet, forlorn
little yellow street—he found a tiny house of two
rooms and a tiny garden. This would cost five pounds
a year. Mazzaiba lent the furniture—and when I
left, M. was busily skipping back and forth from
Rabato to Valletta, arranging his little home, and
very pleased with it. He was also being very Maltese,
and rather anti-British, as is essential, apparently,
when one is not a Britisher and finds oneself in any
part of the British Empire. M. was very much the
American gentleman.

Well, I was thankful to be home again and to
know that he was safely shut up in that beastly
island. He wrote me letters, saying how he loved it
all, how he would go down to the sea—five or six
miles' walk—at dawn, and stay there all day, studying Maltese and writing for the newspapers. The life
was fascinating, the summer was blisteringly hot,

and the Maltese were *most* attractive, especially when they knew you were not British. Such good-looking fellows, too, and do anything you want. Wouldn't I come and spend a month? I did not answer—felt I had had enough. Came a postcard from M.: "I haven't had a letter from you, nor any news at all. I am afraid you are ill, and feel so anxious. Do write—" But, no, I didn't want to write.

During August and September and half October we were away in the north. I forgot my little friend; hoped he was gone out of my life. But I had that fatal sinking feeling that he *hadn't* really gone out of it yet.

In the beginning of November a little letter from Don Bernardo—did I know that M. had committed suicide in Malta? Following that, a scrubby Maltese newspaper, posted by Salonia, with a marked notice "The suicide of an American gentleman at Rabato. Yesterday the American M. M., a well-built man in the prime of life, was found dead in his bed in his house at Rabato. By the bedside was a bottle containing poison. The deceased had evidently taken his life by swallowing prussic acid. Mr. M. had been staying for some months on the island, studying the language and the conditions, with a view to writing a book. It is understood that financial difficulties were the cause of this lamentable event."

Then Mazzaiba wrote asking me what I knew of M., and saying the latter had borrowed money which he, Mazzaiba, would like to recover. I replied at once, and then received the following letter from Salonia:

Valletta, 20 November 1920.

My dear Mr. Lawrence,

    Some time back I mailed you our *Daily Malta Chronicle* which gave an account of the death of M. I hope you have received same. As the statements therein given were very vague and not quite correct, please accept the latter part of this letter as a more correct version.

    The day before yesterday Mazzaiba received your letter, which he gave me to read. As you may suppose, we were very much astonished by its general purport. Mazzaiba will be writing to you in a few days; in the meantime I volunteered to give you the details you asked for.

    Mazzaiba and I have done all in our power to render M.'s stay here as easy and pleasant as possible from the time we first met him in your company at the Great Britain Hotel. [This is not correct. They were already quite friendly with M. before that motor-drive, when I saw these two Maltese for the first time.] He lived in an embarrassed mood since then, and though we helped him as best we could both morally and financially, he never confided to us his troubles. To this very day we cannot but look on his coming here and his stay amongst us, to say the least of the way he left us, as a huge farce wrapped up in mystery, a painful experience unsolicited by either of us, and a cause of grief unrequited except by our own personal sense of duty toward a stranger.

Mazzaiba out of mere respect did not tell me of his commitments toward M. until about a month ago, and this he did in a most confidential and private manner merely to put me on my guard, thinking, and rightly, too, that M. would be falling on me next time for funds; Mazzaiba having already given about £55 and would not possibly commit himself any further. Of course, we found him all along a perfect gentleman. Naturally, he hated the very idea that we or anybody else in Malta should look upon him in any other light. He never asked directly, though Mazzaiba (later myself) was always quick enough to interpret rightly what he meant and obliged him forthwith.

At this stage, to save the situation, he made up a scheme that the three of us should exploit the commercial possibilities in Morocco. It very nearly materialized, everything was ready, I was to go with him to Morocco, Mazzaiba to take charge of affairs here and to dispose of transactions we initiated there. Fortunately, for lack of the necessary funds the idea had to be dropped, and there it ended, thank God, after a great deal of trouble I had in trying to set it well on foot.

Last July, the police, according to our law, advised him that he was either to find a surety or to deposit a sum of money with them, as otherwise at the expiration of his three months' stay he would be compelled to leave the place. Money he had none, so he asked Mazzaiba to stand as surety. Mazzaiba could not, as he was already guarantor for his alien cousins who were here at the time. Mazzaiba (not M.) asked me and I complied, thinking that the responsibility was just moral and only exacted as a matter of form.

When, as stated before, Mazzaiba told me that M. owed him £55 and that he owed his grocer and others at Notabile (the old town, of which Rabato is the suburb) over £10, I thought I might as well look up my guarantee and see if I was directly responsible for any debts he incurred here. The words of his declaration which I endorsed stated that "I hereby solemnly promise that I will not be a burden to the inhabitants of these islands, etc.," and deeming unpaid debts to be more or less a burden, I decided to withdraw my guarantee, which I did on the 23rd ult. The reason I gave to the police was that he was outliving his income and that I did not intend to shoulder any financial responsibility in the matter. On the same day I wrote to him up at Notabile, saying that for family reasons I was compelled to withdraw his surety. He took my letter in the sense implied and no way offended at my procedure.

M., in his resourceful way, knowing that he would with great difficulty find another guarantor, wrote at once to the police saying that he understood from Mr. Salonia that he (S) had withdrawn his guarantee, but as he (M) would be leaving the island in about three weeks' time (still intending to exploit Morocco) he begged the Commissioner to allow him this period of grace, without demanding a new surety. In fact he asked me to find him a cheap passage to Gib. in an ingoing tramp steamer. The police did not reply to his letter at all; no doubt they had everything ready and well thought out. He was alarmed in not receiving an acknowledgment, and, knowing full well what he imminently expected at the hands of the Italian police, he decided to prepare for the last act of his drama.

We had not seen him for three or four days when he came to Mazzaiba's office on Wednesday, 3rd inst., in the forenoon. He stayed there for some time talking on general subjects and looking somewhat more excited than usual. He went up to town alone at noon as Mazzaiba went to Singlea. I was not with them in the morning, but in the afternoon about 4:30, whilst I was talking to Mazzaiba in his office, M. again came in looking very excited, and, being closing time, we went up, the three of us, to town, and there left him in the company of a friend.

On Thursday morning, 4th inst., at about 10 a.m., two detectives in plain clothes met him in a street at Notabile. One of them quite casually went up to him and said very civilly that the inspector of police wished to see him *re* a guarantee or something, and that he was to go with him to the police station. This was an excuse, as the detective had about him a warrant for his arrest for frauding an hotel in Rome, and that he was to be extradited at the request of the authorities in Italy. M. replied that as he was in his sandals he would dress up and go with them immediately, and, accompanying him to his house at No. 1 Strada S. Pietro, they allowed him to enter. He locked the door behind him, leaving them outside.

A few minutes later he opened his bedroom window and dropped a letter addressed to Don Bernardo which he asked a boy in the street to post for him, and immediately closed the window again. One of the detectives picked up the letter and we do not know to this day if same was posted at all. Some time elapsed and he did not come out. The detectives were by this time very uneasy and as another police official came up they decided to burst open the door. As the door did not give way they got a ladder and climbed over the roof, and there they found M. in his bedroom dying from poisoning, outstretched on his bed and a glass of water close by. A priest was immediately called in who had just time to administer extreme unction before he died at 11:45 a.m.

At 8:00 a.m. the next day his body was admitted for

examination at the Floriana Civil Hospital and death was certified to be from poisoning with hydrocyanic acid. His age was given as 44, being buried on his birthday (7th Novr.), with R. Catholic rites at the expense of *his friends in Malta*.

Addenda: Contents of Don Bernardo's letter:
"I leave it to you and to Gabriel Mazzaiba to arrange my affairs. I cannot live any longer. Pray for me."

Document found on his writing-table:
"In case of my unexpected death inform American consul.

"I want to buried first class, my wife will pay.

"My little personal belongings to be delivered to my wife. (Address.)

"My best friend here, Gabriel Mazzaiba, inform him. (Address.)

"My literary executor N. D. (Address.)

"All manuscripts and books for N. D. I leave my literary property to N. D. to whom half the results are to accrue. The other half my debts are to be paid with:

"Furniture etc. belong to Coleiro, Floriana.

"Silver spoons etc. belong to Gabriel Mazzaiba. (Address.)"

The American Consul is in charge of all his personal belongings. I am sure he will be pleased to give you any further details you may require. By the way, his wife refused to pay his burial expenses, but five of his friends in Malta undertook to give him a decent funeral. His mourners were: the consul, the vice-consul, Mr. A., an American citizen, Gabriel Mazzaiba, and myself.

Please convey to Mrs. Lawrence an expression of our sincere esteem and high regard and you will kindly accept equally our warmest respects, whilst soliciting any information you would care to pass on to us regarding the late M.

Believe me, my dear Mr. Lawrence, etc.

[Mrs. M. refunded the burial expenses through the American consul about two months after her husband's death.]

When I had read this letter the world seemed to stand still for me. I knew that in my own soul I had said: "Yes, he must die if he cannot find his own way." But for all that, now I *realized* what it must have meant to be the hunted, desperate man: everything seemed to stand still. I could, by giving half my money, have saved his life. I had chosen not to save his life.

Now, after a year has gone by, I keep to my choice. I still would not save his life. I respect him for dying when he was cornered. And for this reason I feel still connected with him: still have this to discharge, to get his book published, and to give him his place, to present him just as he was as far as I knew him myself.

The worst thing I have against him is that he abused the confidence, the kindness, and the generosity of unsuspecting people like Mazzaiba. He did not *want* to, perhaps. But he did it. And he leaves Mazzaiba swindled, distressed, confused, and feeling sold in the best part of himself. What next? What is one to feel towards one's strangers, after having known M.? It is this Judas treachery to *ask* for sympathy and for generosity, to take it when given—and then: "Sorry, but anybody may make a mistake!" It is this betraying with a kiss which makes me still say: "He should have died sooner." No, I would not help to keep him alive, not if I had to choose again. I would let him go over into death. He shall and should die, and so should all his sort: and so they will. There are so many kiss-giving Judases. He was not a criminal: he was obviously well intentioned: but a Judas every time, selling the good feeling he had tried to arouse, and had aroused, for any handful of silver he could get. A little loving vampire!

Yesterday arrived the manuscript of the Legion, from Malta. It is exactly two years since I read it first in the monastery. Then I was moved and rather horrified. Now I am chiefly amused; because in my mind's eye is the figure of M. in the red trousers and the blue coat with lappets turned up, swinging like a little indignant pigeon across the drill yards and into the canteen of Bel-Abbes. He *is* so indignant, so righteously and morally indignant, and so funny. All the horrors of the actuality fade before the indignation, his little, tuppenny indignation.

Oh, M. is a prime hypocrite. *How* loudly he rails against the Boches! *How* great his enthusiasm for the pure, the spiritual Allied cause. Just so long as he is in Africa, and it suits his purpose! His scorn for the German tendencies of the German legionaries: even Count de R. secretly leans towards Ger-

many. "Blood is thicker than water," says our hero
glibly. Some blood, thank God. Apparently not his
own. For according to all showing he was, by blood,
pure German: father and mother: even Hohenzollern
blood!!! Pure German! Even his speech, his *mother-
tongue,* was German and not English! And then the
little mongrel—!

But perhaps something happens to blood when
once it has been taken to America.

And then, once he is in Valbonne, lo, a change!
Where now is sacred France and the holy Allied
Cause! Where is our hero's fervour? It is *worse than*
Bel-Abbes! Yes, indeed, far less human, more hide-
ously cold. One is driven by very rage to wonder if
he was really a spy, a German spy whom Germany
cast off because he was no good.

The little *gentleman!* God damn his white-blooded
gentility. The legionaries must have been gentlemen,
that they didn't kick him every day to the lavatory
and back.

"You are a journalist?" said the colonel.

"No, a *littérateur,*" said M. perkily.

"That is something more?" said the Colonel.

Oh, I would have given a lot to have seen it and
heard it. The *littérateur!* Well, I hope this book will
establish his fame as such. I hope the editor, if it
gets one, won't alter any more of the marvellously
staggering sentences and the joyful French mistakes.
The *littérateur!*—the impossible little pigeon!

But the Bel-Abbes part is alive and interesting.
It should be read only by those who have the stomach.
Ugly, foul—alas, it is no uglier and no fouler than
the reality. M. himself was near enough to being a
scoundrel, thief, forger, etc., etc.—what lovely
strings of names he hurls at them!—to be able to
appreciate their company. He himself was such a
liar, that he was not taken in. But his conceit as a
gentleman *keeping up appearances* gave him a real
standpoint from which to see the rest. The book is in
its way a real creation. But I would hate it to be
published and taken at its face value, with M. as a

spiritual dove among vultures of lust. Let us first
put a pinch of salt on the tail of this dove. What
he did do in the way of vice, even in Bel-Abbes, I
never chose to ask him.

Yes, yes, he sings another note when he is planted
right among the sacred Allies, with never a German near. Then the gorgeousness goes out of his
indignation. He takes it off with the red trousers.
Now he is just a sordid little figure in filthy corduroys. There is no vice to purple his indignation, the
little holy liar. There is only sordidness and automatic, passionless, colourless awful mud. When all is
said and done, mud, cold, hideous, foul, engulfing
mud, up to the waist, this is the final symbol of the
Great War. Hear some of the horrified young soldiers. They dare hardly speak of it yet.

The Valbonne part is worse, really, than the Bel-
Abbes part. Passionless, barren, utterly, coldly foul
and hopeless. The ghastly emptiness, and the slow
mud-vortex, the brink of it.

Well, now M. has gone himself. Yes, and he would
be gone in the common mud and dust himself, if it
were not that the blood still beats warm and hurt
and kind in some few hearts. M. "hinted" to Mazzaiba for money, in Malta, and Mazzaiba gave it to
him, thinking him a man in distress. He thought him
a gentleman, and lovable, and in trouble! And Mazzaiba—it isn't his real name, but there he is, real
enough—still has this feeling of grief for M. So
much so that now he has had the remains taken from
the public grave in Malta, and buried in his own,
the Mazzaiba grave, so that they shall not be lost.
For my part, I would have said that the sooner they
mingled with the universal dust, the better. But one
is glad to see a little genuine kindness and gentle-
ness, even if it is wasted on the bones of that selfish
little scamp of a M. He despised his "physical friendships," though he didn't forgo them. So why should
anyone rescue his physique from the public grave?

But there you are—there was his power: to arouse
affection and a certain tenderness in the hearts of

others, for himself. And on this he traded. One sees the trick working all the way through the Legion book. God knows how much warm kindness, generosity, was showered on him during the course of his forty-odd years. And selfish little scamp, he took it as a greedy boy takes cakes off a dish, quickly, to make the most of his opportunity while it lasted. And the cake once eaten: *buona sera!* He patted his own little paunch and felt virtuous. Merely physical feeling, you see! He had a way of saying "physical" —a sort of American way, as if it were spelt "fisacal" —that made me want to kick him.

Not that he was mean, while he was about it. No, he would give very freely: even a little ostentatiously, always feeling that he was being a *liberal gentleman*. Ach, the liberality and the gentility he prided himself on! *Ecco!* And he gave a large tip, with a little winsome smile. But in his heart of hearts it was always himself he was thinking of, while he did it. Playing his role of the gentleman who was awfully nice to everybody—so long as they were nice to him, or so long as it served his advantage. Just private charity!

Well, poor devil, he is dead: which is all the better. He had his points, the courage of his own terrors, quick-wittedness, sensitiveness to certain things in his surroundings. I prefer him, scamp as he is, to the ordinary respectable person. He ran his risks: he *had* to be running risks with the police, apparently. And he poisoned himself rather than fall into their clutches. I like him for that. And I like him for the sharp and quick way he made use of every one of his opportunities to get out of that beastly army. There I admire him: a courageous, isolated little devil, facing his risks, and like a good rat, *determined* not to be trapped. I won't forgive him for trading on the generosity of others, and so dropping poison into the heart of all warm-blooded faith. But I am glad after all that Mazzaiba has rescued his bones from the public grave. I wouldn't have done it myself, because I don't forgive him his "fisacal" impudence and parasitism. But I am glad Mazzaiba has done it. And, for my part, I will put his Legion book before the world if I can. Let him have his place in the world's consciousness.

Let him have his place, let his word be heard. He went through vile experiences: he looked them in the face, braved them through, and kept his manhood in spite of them. For manhood is a strange quality, to be found in human rats as well as in hot-blooded men. M. carried the human consciousness through circumstances which would have been too much for me. I would have died rather than be so humiliated, I could never have borne it. Other men, I know, went through worse things in the war. But then, horrors, like pain, are their own anaesthetic. Men lose their normal consciousness, and go through in a sort of delirium. The bit of Stendhal which Dos Passos quotes in front of *Three Soldiers* is frighteningly true. There are certain things which are *so* bitter, *so* horrible, that the contemporaries just cannot know them, cannot contemplate them. So it is with a great deal of the late war. It was so foul, and humanity in Europe fell suddenly into such ignominy and inhuman ghastliness, that we shall *never* fully realize what it was. We just cannot bear it. We haven't the soul-strength to contemplate it.

And yet, humanity can only finally conquer by realizing. It is human destiny, since Man fell into consciousness and self-consciousness, that we can only go forward step by step through realization, full, bitter, conscious realization. This is true of all the great terrors and agonies and anguishes of life: sex, and war, and even crime. When Flaubert in his story—it is so long since I read it—makes his saint have to kiss the leper, and naked clasp the leprous awful body against his own, that is what we must at last do. It is the great command, *Know Thyself*. We've got to *know* what sex is, let the sentimentalists wiggle as they like. We've got to know the greatest and most shattering human passions, let the puritans squeal as they like for screens. And we've got to know humanity's criminal tendency, look straight at humanity's great deeds of crime against the soul. We have to fold this horrible leper against our naked warmth, because life and the throbbing blood and the believing soul are greater even than leprosy. Knowledge, true knowledge, is like vaccination. It prevents the continuing of ghastly moral disease.

And so it is with the war. Humanity in Europe fell horribly into a hatred of the living soul, in the war. There is no gainsaying it. We all fell. Let us not try to wriggle out of it. We fell into hideous depravity of hating the human soul; a purulent smallpox of the spirit we had. It was shameful, shameful, shameful, in every country and in all of us. Some tried to resist, and some didn't. But we were all drowned in shame. A purulent smallpox of the vicious spirit, vicious against the deep soul that pulses in the blood.

We haven't got over it. The smallpox sores are running yet in the spirit of mankind. And we have got to take this putrid spirit to our bosom. There's nothing else for it. Take the foul rotten spirit of mankind, full of the running sores of the war, to our bosom, and cleanse it there. Cleanse it not with blind love; ah, no, that won't help. But with bitter and wincing realization. We have to take the disease into our consciousness and let it go through our soul, like some virus. We have got to realize. And then we can surpass.

M. went where I could never go. He carried the human consciousness unbroken through circumstances I could not have borne. It is not heroism to rush on death. It is cowardice to accept a martyrdom today. That is the feeling one has at the end of Dos Passos's book. To let oneself be absolutely trapped? Never! I prefer M. He drew himself out of the thing he loathed, despised, and feared. He fought it, for his own spirit and liberty. He fought it open-eyed. He went through. They were more publicly heroic, they won war medals. But the lonely terrified courage of the isolated spirit which grits its teeth and stares the horrors in the face and *will* not succumb to them, but fights its way through them, *knowing* that it must surpass them: this is the rarest courage. And this courage M. had: and the man in the Dos Passos book didn't *quite* have it. And so, though M. poisoned himself, and I would not wish him *not* to have poisoned himself; though as far as warm life goes, I don't forgive him; yet, as far as the eternal and unconquerable spirit of man goes, I am with him through eternity. I am grateful to him; he beat out for me boundaries of human experience which I could not have beaten out for myself. The *human* traitor he was. But he was not traitor to the spirit. In the great spirit of human consciousness he was a hero, little, quaking and heroic: a strange, quaking little star.

Even the dead ask only for *justice:* not for praise or exoneration. Who dares humiliate the dead with excuses for their living? I hope I may do M. justice; and I hope his restless spirit may be appeased. I do not try to forgive. The living blood knows no forgiving. Only the overweening spirit takes on itself to dole out forgiveness. But justice is a sacred human right. The overweening spirit pretends to perch above justice. But I am a man, not a spirit, and men with blood that throbs and throbs and throbs can only live at length by being just, can only die in peace if they have justice. Forgiveness gives the whimpering dead no rest. Only deep, true justice.

There is M.'s manuscript then, like a map of the lower places of mankind's activities. There is the war: foul, foul, unutterably foul. As foul as M. says. Let us make up our minds about it.

It is the only help: to realize, *fully,* and then make up our minds. The war was *foul.* As long as I am a man, I say it and assert it, and further I say, as long as I am a man such a war shall never occur again. It shall not, and it shall not. All modern militarism is foul. It shall go. A man I am, and above machines, and it shall go, forever, because I have found it vile, vile, too vile ever to experience again. Cannons shall go. Never again shall trenches be dug. They *shall* not, for I am a man, and such things are within the power of man, to break and make. I have said it, and as long as blood beats in my veins, I mean it. Blood beats in the veins of many men who mean it as well as I.

Man perhaps *must* fight. Mars, the great god of war, will be a god for ever. Very well. Then if fight you must, fight you shall, and without engines, without machines. Fight if you like, as the Roman fought, with swords and spears, or like the Red Indian, with bows and arrows and knives and war paint. But never again shall you fight with the foul, base, fearful, monstrous machines of war which man invented for the last war. You shall not. The diabolic mechanisms are man's, and I am a man. Therefore they are mine. And I smash them into oblivion. With every means in my power, *except* the means of these machines, I smash them into oblivion. I am at war! I, a man, am at war!—with these foul machines and contrivances that men have conjured up. Men have conjured them up. I, a man, will conjure them down again. Won't I? But I will! I am not one man, I am many, I am most.

So much for the war! So much for M.'s manuscript. Let it be read. It is not this that will do harm, but sloppy sentiment and cant. Take the bitterness and cleanse the blood.

Now would you believe it, that little scamp M. spent over a hundred pounds of borrowed money during his four months in Malta, when his expenses, he boasted to me, need not have been more than a pound a week, once he got into the little house in Notabile? That is, he spent at least seventy pounds too much. Heaven knows what he did with it, apart from "guzzling." And this hundred pounds must be paid back in Malta. Which it never will be, unless this manuscript pays it back. Pay the gentleman's last debts, if no others.

He had to be a gentleman. I didn't realize till after his death. I never suspected him of royal blood. But there you are, you never know where it will crop

out. He was the grandson of an emperor. His mother
was the illegitimate daughter of the German Kaiser;
D. says, of the old Kaiser Wilhelm I, Don Bernardo
says, of Kaiser Friedrich Wilhelm, father of the
present ex-Kaiser. She was born in Berlin on October
31, 1845; and her portrait, by Paul, now hangs in a
gallery in Rome. Apparently there had been some
injustice against her in Berlin, for she seems once
to have been in the highest society there, and to have
attended at court. Perhaps she was discreetly ban-
ished by Wilhelm II, hence M.'s hatred of that mon-
arch. She lies buried in the Protestant Cemetery in
Rome, where she died in 1912, with the words *Filia
Regis* on her tomb. M. adored her, and she him. Part
of his failings one can *certainly* ascribe to the fact
that he was an only son, an adored son, in whose
veins the mother imagined only royal blood. And
she must have thought him so beautiful, poor thing!
Ah, well, they are both dead. Let us be just and
wish them Lethe.

M. himself was born in New York, November 7,
1876; so at least it says on his passport. He entered
the Catholic Church in England in 1902. His father
was a Mr. L. M., married to the mother in 1867.

So poor M. had Hohenzollern blood in his veins:
close kin to the ex-Kaiser Wilhelm. Well, that itself
excuses him a great deal: because of the cruel illu-
sion of importance *manqué,* which it must have given
him. He never breathed a word of this to me. Yet
apparently it is accepted at the monastery, the great
monastery which knows most European secrets of
any political significance. And for myself, I believe
it is true. And if he was a scamp and a treacherous
little devil, he had also qualities of nerve and breed-
ing undeniable. He faced his way through that
Legion experience: royal nerves dragging themselves
through the sewers, without giving way. But, alas
for royal blood! Like most other blood, it has
gradually gone white, during our spiritual era.
Bunches of nerves! And whitish, slightly acid blood.
And no bowels of deep compassion and kindliness.

Only charity—a little more than kin, and less than kind.

Also, M.! Ich grüsse dich, in der Ewigkeit. Aber hier, im Herzblut, hast du Gift und Leid nachgelassen —to use your own romantic language.

CONTRIBUTORS

NELSON ALGREN won the first National Book Award for his novel *The Man with the Golden Arm*. Among his other books are *A Walk on the Wild Side, Never Come Morning*, and *The Neon Wilderness*.

LOUIS GUILLOUX is a French writer whose newest book is *La Bataille perdue*. An earlier novel was published in America as *Bitter Victory*.

JULES FEIFFER is the author of three cartoon books—*Sick, Sick, Sick, Passionella*, and *The Explainers*—whose on-target satire has reached large audiences.

GRACE PALEY'S collection of stories, *The Little Disturbances of Man*, was greeted as the work of a brilliant new writer. "Faith in the Afternoon" is part of her novel in progress.

BARRY SPACKS has published in *Antioch Review, Atlantic Monthly, Poetry, Playboy, Chicago Review*, and other periodicals.

GEORGE P. ELLIOTT has taught at Cornell and Barnard and is now at the Writers Workshop of the State University of Iowa. His published novel is *Parktilden Village;* another is in preparation.

SOL YURICK is a young, hitherto unpublished writer.

GEORGE BOGIN has published poetry in *The Nation, Prairie Schooner*, and *Contemporary Reader*.

RICHARD G. STERN teaches English at the University of Chicago. His first novel, *Golk*, was published in 1960.

CYNTHIA OZICK'S work—poetry, essays, and fiction—has appeared in a number of magazines, among them *Botteghe Oscure, San Francisco Review, Evergreen Review*, and *Commentary*.

KEITH BOTSFORD is an editor of *The Noble Savage* and the author of *The Eighth-Best-Dressed Man in the World*, a novel. His next book is *Benvenuto*.

FREDERICK SEIDEL'S "His Uncle Henry Levy at His Coalyards"
is a section of a longer poem, "Homecoming to St. Louis."

BERNARD A. FARBAR is a graduate of Dartmouth and a former
student at the Sorbonne. "Love" is his first publication.

DAN WAKEFIELD'S reportage appears in a number of magazines. He is the author of *Island in the City*, a study of New
York Puerto Ricans.

D. H. LAWRENCE'S "The Portrait of M. M." was originally
published as the preface to Maurice Magnus's *Memoirs of
the Foreign Legion*.

thenoblesavage thenoblesavage thenoblesava
thenoblesavage thenoblesavage thenoblesava
thenoblesavage thenoblesavage thenoblesava
thenoblesavage thenoblesavage thenoblesava
thenoblesavage thenoblesavage thenoblesava
thenoblesavage thenoblesavage thenoblesava
thenoblesavage thenoblesavage thenoblesava
thenoblesavage thenoblesavage thenoblesava
thenoblesavage thenoblesavage thenoblesava
thenoblesavage thenoblesavage thenoblesava
thenoblesavage thenoblesavage thenoblesava
thenoblesavage thenoblesavage thenoblesava
thenoblesavage thenoblesavage thenoblesava
thenoblesavage thenoblesavage thenoblesava
thenoblesavage thenoblesavage thenoblesava
thenoblesavage thenoblesavage thenoblesav
thenoblesavage thenoblesavage thenoblesava
thenoblesavage thenoblesavage thenoblesava
thenoblesavage thenoblesavage thenoblesava
thenoblesavage thenoblesavage thenoblesava
thenoblesavage thenoblesavage thenoblesava
thenoblesavage thenoblesavage thenoblesava
thenoblesavage thenoblesavage thenoblesava
thenoblesavage thenoblesavage thenoblesava
thenoblesavage thenoblesavage thenoblesava
thenoblesavage thenoblesavage thenoblesav
thenoblesavage thenoblesavage thenoblesav
thenoblesavage thenoblesavage thenoblesav
thenoblesavage thenoblesavage thenoblesav
thenoblesavage thenoblesavage thenoblesav
thenoblesavage thenoblesavage thenoblesav
thenoblesavage thenoblesavage thenoblesav
thenoblesavage thenoblesavage thenoblesav
thenoblesavage thenoblesavage thenoblesav
thenoblesavage thenoblesavage thenoblesav
enoblesavage thenoblesavage thenoblesav